yourself

beauty

teach®
yourself

beauty
yvette redmond

For UK order enquiries: please contact Bookpoint Ltd, 130 Milton Park, Abingdon, Oxon, OX14 4SB. Telephone: +44 (0) 1235 827720. Fax: +44 (0) 1235 400454. Lines are open 09.00–17.00, Monday to Saturday, with a 24-hour message answering service. Details about our titles and how to order are available at www.teachyourself.co.uk

For USA order enquiries: please contact McGraw-Hill Customer Services, PO Box 545, Blacklick, OH 43004-0545, USA. Telephone: 1-800-722-4726. Fax: 1-614-755-5645.

For Canada order enquiries: please contact McGraw-Hill Ryerson Ltd, 300 Water St, Whitby, Ontario, L1N 9B6, Canada. Telephone: 905 430 5000. Fax: 905 430 5020.

Long renowned as the authoritative source for self-guided learning – with more than 50 million copies sold worldwide – the **teach yourself** series includes over 500 titles in the fields of languages, crafts, hobbies, business, computing and education.

British Library Cataloguing in Publication Data: a catalogue record for this title is available from the British Library.

Library of Congress Catalog Card Number: on file.

First published in UK 1994 by Hodder Education, 338 Euston Road, London, NW1 3BH.

First published in US 1994 by The McGraw-Hill Companies, Inc.

This edition published 2006.

The **teach yourself** name is a registered trade mark of Hodder Headline.

Copyright © 2006 Yvette Redmond

Typeset by Transet Limited, Coventry, England.
Printed in Great Britain for Hodder Education, a division of Hodder Headline, 338 Euston Road, London, NW1 3BH, by Cox & Wyman Ltd, Reading, Berkshire.

The publisher has used its best endeavours to ensure that the URLs for external websites referred to in this book are correct and active at the time of going to press. However, the publisher and the author have no responsibility for the websites and can make no guarantee that a site will remain live or that the content will remain relevant, decent or appropriate.

Hodder Headline's policy is to use papers that are natural, renewable and recyclable products and made from wood grown in sustainable forests. The logging and manufacturing processes are expected to conform to the environmental regulations of the country of origin.

Impression number   10 9 8 7 6 5 4 3 2 1
Year   2010 2009 2008 2007 2006

contents

foreword

Yvette's going to give you a recipe for baking the perfect 'beauty cake', covering all the ingredients, from the basics to the icing and even how to 'serve' it! She is the perfect cook to guide you through the process and I have known her for over 15 years.

We first met when I took her on as a model. Yvette was one of the first girls I represented at Storm, and she subsequently – after a very successful career as a model – trained as a make-up artist and a fully qualified holistic therapist. We have always stayed in touch and it has been a real pleasure for me to witness all the qualities that made Yvette such a successful model ensure that she succeeds similarly in her new career – a mixture of professionalism and enthusiasm, which is one of the secret ingredients in her own 'beauty cake'.

Yvette is an intelligent, enthusiastic, upbeat and inspiring person – all gifts that she brings to this thoroughly complete and insightful 'recipe' book for a lasting and an achievable 'beauty cake'. Her approach to looking and feeling good is straightforward and easy to follow – her advice is both real and realistic, something we can all appreciate in our busy and hectic lives.

The combination of Yvette's professional make-up expertise, combined with her years of experience in the fashion industry as a model, bring to this recipe some very 'special ingredients' and some fantastic insider tips, making this a truly must-have book, for all of us!

By Sarah Doukas, Managing Director,
Storm Model Management

acknowledgements

To my wonderful husband James, whose unwavering love and support has made writing this book possible for me to do. To my amazing illustrator Art Jaz, who has literally brought my words to life, thank you for all your hard work. To Sarah Feeley and your red pen, thank you for being my fresh eyes when I couldn't see straight any more and for being like Obi-Wan Kenobi and showing me how to use 'the force'. To my mother Yvonne Iles, thank you for the great start that you gave me both in life and with my skin care and also for teaching me that I could achieve anything that I set my mind to. To my new families: Bill, Christine, Matt, Kate, Tony, Mark, Lise, Alex, Louis and Kristen – thank you for being there. To Sarah Doukas for putting me on the path that ultimately led me here, thank you for your continued help and support. I will always be proud to have been a 'Storm' girl. To Carol Hayes, my agent, thank you for taking care of my career and always being supportive of my choices. To Kevin Hawkins, thank you for your invaluable advice. To Henry Abrahams for all your brilliant advice about exercise. To Lisa Spurrell for being my first ever guinea pig – without you I wouldn't be a make-up artist today. To my mother-in-law Christine Redmond, who used to be a chemistry teacher, for her help with the scientific explanations. To Victoria Roddam, my editor at Hodder – it has been a pleasure working with you.

Thank you to everyone who gave me a quote for my words of wisdom section: Alison Frecknall, Alison Potter, Anna Byas, Bill Nighy, Charlotte Murray, Christine Stephen-Daly, Daniel Sandler, Georgina Bouzova, Lainey Sheridan-Young, Lara Baumann, Marc Ramos, Paul Merritt, Penny Jones, Rebecca Cawse, Sally Penford, Sarah Feeley, Shavata, Sue Feeley, Suzannah Agrippa, Tamara Corin, Tamzin Outhwaite and Yvonne Iles.

Thank you to all the PRs who have been so helpful and supportive with this project: Abigail Segall at Freedom, Barbie Kaffel at Estée Lauder, Erica Molloy at Urban Retreats Ltd, Faith Loh at Purple, Jessica Lawther at Prescriptives/Créme de la Mer, Jini Sanassy at klipatrick, Kim Young at Clinique, Linsey Reay at Bobbi Brown, Liz Ampairee at Kenneth Green Associates and Mary Kate at Wizard.

Finally to all the make-up artists, hairdressers, photographers and clients with whom I have ever worked – for helping to make my career what it has been; without which I would never have been able to write this book.

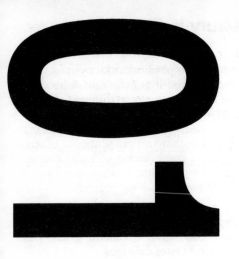

01

what are the basic ingredients?

In this chapter you will learn:
- my beauty recipe
- how the body works
- how exposure to free radicals and sun affects your body
- how nutrition, hydration and sleep redress the balance
- how to detox and minimize stress in your life.

Introduction: beauty is like baking a cake

Beauty is about so much more than physical attractiveness, it is more than just a visual aesthetic and it is definitely more than skin deep. Beauty can mean different things to different people, but at its essence there is always a truth and an individuality. Perfection isn't necessarily beautiful, but individuality almost always is. Beauty is not something that you can score out of ten, it is something that radiates as a combination of many things. Personality, strength of character, health, vitality, confidence and uniqueness are what truly make someone beautiful.

My philosophy of beauty is that it's a bit like baking a cake. If you get the ingredients right and you follow the recipe, you should end up with a pretty good cake – something that has risen well, has a good colour and tastes delicious.

Get some of your ingredients wrong, however, and your cake could end up sunk in the middle, burnt at the edges and not tasting so great.

When a cake is good, it often doesn't need any icing to make it look or taste any better. When a cake is not so great, you can vastly improve its appearance with icing and make it look amazing.

For me, beauty is like 'good cake' and make-up is like icing. My recipe for a good beauty cake includes all the ingredients that are involved in taking good care of ourselves. When we take good care of ourselves, we are supporting and encouraging the body and mind to function at their absolute best. We will be healthy and this will show in our appearance, which will be youthful, radiant and of course, more beautiful. My icing recipes can be used in a minimal way, as just simple presentation, or as a tool to make a not so great 'cake' look (and feel) much better!

Getting our mind and body to be able to function at their best involves a combination of getting enough sleep, drinking enough water, getting enough nutrients from our food, getting enough exercise, having good posture, looking after the skin on our bodies and our faces, having a positive outlook and avoiding as many things as possible that cause us damage.

Just like in baking, it's the balance of these ingredients that effects how the 'cake' turns out, in the same way that good chefs don't just follow basic recipes – they know how to adapt and get good results, even if the ingredients are slightly different. If you can get the balance of these life ingredients right, you will end up with a good beauty 'cake'.

We are all human, and although the plan might be great, sometimes sticking to it is the hard part. This book provides you with the information that you need to be able to make informed and intelligent choices about how to get the most out of your life and fulfil your own beauty potential. It's not a rule book. Think of it more as a guide; the balance part is up to you.

The world of beauty can be quite overwhelming sometimes. We know that we want to look and feel our best, but sometimes we just don't know where to start. Whatever your skin type or tone, whatever your age or your style, whether you are a make-up virgin or a make-up junkie, whether this is all new to you, or you would simply like a fresh approach to your routine – I have drawn upon all the knowledge that I have acquired in my 18 years in the fashion and beauty industry (ten years as a model and eight as a make-up artist) and I hope to be able to give you all the tools and the know-how to look and feel good on every occasion.

I use all of these techniques when I am at work. Sometimes this could be doing makeovers on the television for programmes such as *The Salon*, *Big Brother's Little Brother* and *Secrets of the Sexes*. It could also be shooting models for magazines such as *Cosmopolitan*, *New Woman*, *Now*, *Hello*, *OK*, *Tatler* and *Vogue*. I also make up celebrities for magazine shoots and TV interviews. Bands with whom I have worked include Blue and Liberty X. Actors with whom I have worked include Bill Nighy (*Love Actually*), Donald Sutherland (*Pride and Prejudice*), Goran Visnijc (*ER*), Max Beesley (*Hotel Babylon*), Kenneth Brannagh (*The Magic Flute*), Christian Slater (*True Romance*), Emilio Estevez (*The Breakfast Club*) and of course, my husband, James Redmond (*Casualty*). Actresses with whom I have worked include Thandie Newton (*Crash*), Linda Cardellini (*ER*), Kelly Rowan (*The O.C.*), Alison Janney (*The West Wing*), Alison Hannigan (*American Pie*), Tamzin Outhwaite (*Hotel Babylon*), Christine Stephen-Daly (*Cutting It*) and Abi Titmuss.

I have tried to make everything as simple and straightforward as possible. There is some science stuff, but only where it is fundamental to understanding how to get the best out of your body or your skin. By the end of the book, you should have discovered some options for changing the routine of your life, or maybe for boosting your confidence. You may decide to try to eat more healthily or at least have a more healthy relationship with food. You may be able to accept yourself a bit more or at least have learnt some clever ways to make the most of your best bits. Either way, I have tried to keep my techniques as simple and basic as possible and, I hope, easy to follow.

As a make-up artist, it has been a bit like baring my soul to give away all my 'secrets', but in doing so, I hope to be able to show people that make-up is not as scary as many people think it is. Most women just want to look as pretty as possible and I think that if you have the right knowledge and the right tools, you can be your own life coach, your own skin-care expert and your own make-up artist, and be not just pretty – you can be beautiful.

Balancing the ingredients

The recipe

Basic cake ingredients:

Free radicals	*minimum, balanced with maximum antioxidants*
Sun	*enough for health, with protection*
Water	*at least two litres per day*
Detox	*when necessary*
Nutritious diet	*five portions of fruit and veg per day*
Sleep	*eight hours a night*
Stress	*minimum*

Icing ingredients:

Body care	*body brush and moisturize daily*
Skin care	*the right kind for you*
Make-up	*as needed or desired*

Presentation:

Good posture	*both sitting and standing*
Yoga	*including breathing and relaxation, as often as necessary*
Exercise	*one hour, three times a week*

Secret ingredients:

Self-esteem	*learn to like yourself and discover your own beauty*
Happiness	*think happy, be happy*

This is obviously the ideal, but let's face it, there aren't many of us out there who could actually live like that! The real secret to making this recipe work is in understanding, like any good chef, that the recipe is only the starting point. The trick is in learning how to work with what you've got, and get the balance right. In the same way that a chef corrects a cake mix that has a bit too much flour by adding a bit more liquid, and still bakes a perfect cake, we too can achieve our beauty potential by learning how to balance our own ingredients. I like to look at it a bit like a points system – e.g. alcohol takes points away, berries put points in. Being bad to yourself takes points away, and makes a bad cake that needs lots of icing, whereas being good to yourself makes a good cake that maybe doesn't need any icing at all. Watch out for being too strict with yourself though – you might end up with a far too healthy-tasting cake that nobody wants to eat – you know the ones I mean – zero sugar, zero fat – taste yucky! It's all about the balance!

Learning how to balance the ingredients also means understanding that they all work as a team to produce the cake and how they all rely on each other. You don't have a good cake if any one of them is missing.

Before I start doing someone's make-up, I can usually tell if they are out of balance somehow, because the first place it shows is in the face.

• Balance = firm skin, bright open eyes, full lips, a defined lip line, an even skin tone.
• Imbalance = skin that looks dull, dry or tight, pores that are really open, eyes that look tired.

If someone's face seems out of balance it often turns out that they have been stressed or unwell, or, perhaps they have been over-indulging in food or alcohol. We don't realize how important our lifestyle and well-being are to our skin. There is no point spending heaps on skin-care products if we aren't going to at least try to take care of our body and mind, because our skin reflects outwardly what is going on inside. If we haven't been eating a well-balanced diet, we might end up with constipation. Toxins get backed up in the body, resulting in skin problems. We can re-balance ourselves by eating some roughage and drinking more water. If we are unhappy, tired or desperate, it will show immediately in our skin. Learning to relax and de-stress does a lot more than just calm the mind, it calms the body and the skin too.

Understanding how to keep everything in balance is what is going to help us achieve our goal. Under balanced circumstances, our bodies function amazingly well and all the ingredients are there for us to have a great cake. This proves that we don't have to spend a fortune to be beautiful. A little bit, spent on the right things, together with some knowledge, understanding and common sense should be all we need to be as beautiful as we can be.

The first step is to understand a little bit about how our bodies work.

How our bodies work

Our bodies are made up of tiny microscopic living cells, and these cells all work together to keep us alive. They way they do this is by maintaining *homeostasis* or balance in the body. Put very simply, this is a two-step process of making energy and removing the waste. In order to function properly, cells need the right balance of water, oxygen, nutrients and rest. Together these ingredients make energy. Whenever energy is made, there is always a waste by-product, and this waste needs to be removed otherwise it causes pollution in the tissues. When the cells are healthy, then so are we, and this is visible in our skin. It's that simple. The right amount of:

water + oxygen + nutrients = healthy cells
= a healthy body and good skin

The waste removal system in our bodies is called the *lymphatic system*. It runs around the body, parallel with the circulatory system (the system that pumps the blood to all the major organs and body parts), it collects any toxins from the blood, tissues and even the tissue spaces between all the cells and conveys them to filtering stations called lymph nodes (more commonly known as glands) which remove any harmful wastes and bacteria ready for excretion (either via sweat, urine or faeces). In this way, the lymphatic system is not just a waste removal system, it is the body's main way of fighting disease, infection and repairing damage. Unlike the circulatory system, which has its own pump (the heart), the lymphatic system relies on muscle action and breathing to propel the fluid around the body. This is one of the reasons why exercise and correct breathing are essential for health and therefore beauty.

If your lymph nodes (glands) feel swollen, that is a sign that they are working extra hard; either your body is trying to fight an infection or it is in toxic overload (too much alcohol, coffee, starchy foods, additives, smoking or overexposure to pesticides). Watch out for toxic overload, because if the toxins aren't flushed out, they can stagnate, leading to things like cellulite. (For some detox ideas, please see page 21.)

When the lymphatic system is working correctly, it can cleanse and purify two litres of lymph every day – this is why we need to drink two litres of water a day, to give the body the water it needs to function at its optimum levels. Insufficient hydration can lead to lymphatic problems. (For more information on hydration, please see page 19.)

The face is often the first place that you would notice sluggish lymphatic drainage: most obviously when you wake up with a hangover and your face is swollen and puffy. The good news is that a simple massage can encourage lymphatic flow and drainage and so help to correct any imbalances. This works not only for the whole body, but also just for the face. There is a detailed face massage routine on pages 98–105.

As well as massage, any boost in circulation (e.g. exercise or yoga, see page 204) can help the body to eliminate waste more efficiently and therefore maintain better balance.

Free radicals (minimum, balanced with maximum antioxidants)

Just like water, oxygen is one of the main factors in the formula for life. The right amount of:

water + oxygen + nutrients = healthy cells
= healthy body and good skin

If we go for even just a few minutes without oxygen, we can die. The trouble is, as with any process of making energy (which is what the body uses the oxygen for), there are waste by-products. These by-products are called 'free radicals'. Until I started writing this book, I couldn't have explained to you what a free radical actually was or what an antioxidant actually did. All I knew, vaguely, was that free radicals were bad and antioxidants were good. I knew that in order to be able to fully explain how the skin ages, why the sun damages us, why certain foods or creams are better for us than others, I needed to understand why free radicals and antioxidants are very important factors in the quest for achieving our beauty potential.

The science bit: In stable atoms and molecules, electrons are paired. Any loss of one of these paired electrons results in the formation of a free radical. A free radical will then try stabilize itself again by attacking anything that it comes into contact with to 'steal' an electron. When an 'attacked' particle loses its electron, a chain reaction begins. Once this process has started, it can cascade and may finally result in the disruption of a living cell.

Because some free radicals are by-products of our natural metabolism (the way our body uses food and fuel to make energy), and sometimes the body's immune system even creates them on purpose to neutralize viruses and bacteria, it's good to know that the body is well equipped to handle about 99 per cent of this naturally occurring free radical action.

However, environmental factors such as pollution, sun radiation and cigarette smoke can lead us to absorb huge amounts of free radicals into our bodies, and this is when damage can occur. These external factors, together with the one per cent that our body can't handle are what result in not only the visible signs of ageing, but also many other health risks.

Environmental sources of free radicals include exposure to:

- Industrial pollution
- Sun exposure – most of us protect ourselves when we are sunbathing; the danger is general day-to-day exposure while walking the dog, shopping, etc.
- Burnt or barbecued food – fat turns to charcoal when it is burnt and charcoal creates free radicals
- Ozone – we see evidence of ozone damage in the changing weather systems and our environment; it is just as harsh on our bodies
- Nitrous oxide – primarily from automobile exhaust
- Heavy metals – such as mercury, cadmium and lead
- Cigarette smoke (both active and passive) – each inhalation of a cigarette multiplies the amount of free radicals that the body has to deal with by 1,000. Everybody knows that smoking is detrimental to general health, but it is also one of the worst things that you can do for your face. Not only does it give you permanent lines around your mouth and dark circles under your eyes, but smoking can age your skin by as much as 10–15 years. It may not show immediately, but just like sun damage, the damage is already done and will show up later, just when you want to look as young as possible

- Alcohol – it leaves the skin dehydrated and interferes with circulation, inhibiting the absorption of vital vitamins and minerals. A hangover is basically a free radical attack on the body.

Prolonged exposure to any of these things will age the skin and wreak havoc with our bodies.

Thankfully, it's not all doom and gloom and the antidote to free radical damage is readily available to us in food, supplements and now in some skin-care treatments. Antioxidants (as the name suggests) are a family of nutrients that can stop the free radical damage from happening. Antioxidants are stable even if they are missing an electron, therefore they can donate electrons to the electron-greedy free radicals and stop the chain reaction of damage. This takes away the stress that free radical action puts on the body, leaving cells free to go about their business and repair existing damage, thus slowing down the ageing process.

Antioxidants to the rescue

- Vitamin C (ascorbic acid) found in: berries, kiwi fruit, citrus fruit, broccoli, cauliflower, Brussels sprouts, cabbage, green leafy vegetables and bell peppers
  (*Note*: because our bodies cannot store vitamin C, the best way to get an adequate supply is to get regular doses via our diet, i.e. lots of fresh fruits and vegetables)

> Top Tip: Kiwi fruits have a much higher concentration of vitamin C than oranges and, unlike many fruits, the kiwi's nutrient content remains intact long after harvesting.

- Vitamin E (alpha tocopherol) found in: nuts, seeds, green leafy vegetables, broccoli, cereals, oats, grains, eggs and olive oil
- Vitamin A (retinol and beta carotene – orange pigment) found in: carrots, apricots, cantaloupe melon, parsley, spinach, kale, and sweet potatoes

> Top Tip: Vitamin A stores in your body can be depleted by infection, so it's a good idea to boost your intake during colds, flu or other viral or bacterial conditions.

- Lutein (yellow pigment) found in: kale, spinach, turnip greens, sweetcorn and egg yolks
- Lycopene (red pigment) found in: tomatoes, guava, rosehip, watermelon and pink grapefruit
- Lignan found in: flax seed, pulses and whole grains
- Coenzyme Q10 found in: sardines, mackerel, meat, spinach broccoli, peanuts, wheat germ whole grains
- Glutathione found in: fish, meat, asparagus, avocado and walnuts
- Flavinoids and polyphenols found in: red wine, red grapes, cranberries, soy and tea. Tea (both green and black) has high flavinoid content and therefore high antioxidant properties. Green tea contains simple flavinoids called catechins, and black tea, which is oxidized, contains more complex flavinoids called theaflavins and thearubigins. Even though the oxidation process modifies the type of flavinoids that are present, the total level, and their overall antioxidant activity is similar in both types of tea.

> Herbs, spices and fruits such as bilberry, turmeric, grape-seed extract, oregano, sage, peppermint, parsley, thyme, lemon balm, clove, allspice, cinnamon and gingko biloba can also provide powerful antioxidant protection for the body. They contain more antioxidants when fresh, but dried are still fairly potent.

Like Batman and Robin, any good superhero has its partner, without whom they couldn't get the job done as well. In the case of antioxidants, Robin would be these minerals:

- Selenium found in Brazil nuts, tuna fish, oysters, flounder, turkey, chicken, wheat germ, brown rice, oatmeal, eggs, sunflower seeds, shrimp and garlic
- Manganese found in nuts, wheat germ, wheat bran, leafy green vegetables, beet tops, pineapple and seeds
- Zinc found in oysters, red meat, pulses, nuts, seafood, seaweed, whole grains, fortified breakfast cereals and dairy products
- Copper found in grains, nuts (particularly Brazil and cashew nuts), meats (liver and kidney), shellfish, legumes (peas and beans) and seeds.

> **Top ten antioxidant foods:**
>
> **1** berries (especially blueberries)
> **2** red kidney beans
> **3** prunes/raisins
> **4** plums
> **5** red grapes
> **6** cruciferous vegetables (like broccoli, cauliflower)
> **7** green leafy vegetables (like kale, spinach)
> **8** russet potatoes
> **9** apples
> **10** tea

Antioxidant recipe ideas

- Breakfast: try *whole grain cereal topped with fresh berries* (blueberries, blackberries, strawberries or raspberries), or a *berry smoothie* (throw a handful of berries into the blender with some fruit juice and maybe a banana)

- Lunch: try an *antioxidant spinach and berry salad*

  Ingredients (serves 4–6):
  - fresh spinach, torn in bite-sized pieces
  - a handful thickly sliced strawberries
  - a handful blueberries
  - 1 small red onion, thinly sliced, pulled into rings
  - a few chopped pecans

- Dinner: as a side to your normal dinner, try *Mediterranean kale*

  Ingredients (Serves 4):
  - 2 medium bunches kale, chopped
  - 2 tablespoons lemon juice
  - 1 teaspoon soy sauce
  - 3 medium cloves garlic, crushed
  - extra virgin olive oil, to taste
  - salt and black pepper, to taste

Directions:

1 Bring lightly salted water to the boil in a steamer with a tight-fitting lid.

2 While water is coming to the boil, fold each kale leaf in half and pull or cut out stem. Chop leaves and rinse in colander.

3 When water comes to the boil, add kale to steamer basket and cover. Steam for 7–10 minutes, until tender.

4 Toss with rest of ingredients and serve.

Top Tip: You don't just have to eat antioxidants; you can also apply them directly onto the skin. Skin creams that are packed full of vitamins can improve the texture of the skin by stimulating the skin's cell renewal processes and smoothing the surface while at the same time combating free radical damage. Results won't be instant, but it is quite possible that after about a month the appearance of lines and wrinkles should be less.

Antioxidant skin-care recipes

Carrot and avocado antioxidant face mask

Ingredients:

- 1 cooked and mashed carrot (cooled)
- 1 mashed avocado
- 125 ml heavy cream
- 1 beaten egg
- 3 tablespoons of honey

Directions:

Mix together until smooth. Apply and leave on face for 10 minutes. Rinse well with warm water.

Honey lemon toner

Ingredients:

- 125 ml fresh lemon juice
- grated zest of one lemon
- 250 ml distilled/purified water
- 125 ml witchhazel
- 1 tablespoon of honey

Directions:

Put all the contents into a bottle or a spray bottle and shake well to emulsify. Shake well before each use. If kept in the fridge, will keep for about a month.

Sun *(enough for health, with protection)*

At least 80 per cent of non-genetic skin ageing is caused by over-exposure to the sun. Ultraviolet (UV) radiation is one of the major creators of free radicals and unprotected exposure causes skin damage and wrinkles, lowers immunity and can lead to cancer. A suntan is how the body tries to protect itself. In reaction to the sun, it produces a pigment called *melanin* and sends it towards the surface of the skin to protect the deeper layers of living skin cells from being burned. Sunburn happens when the skin runs out of melanin to protect it. If you have dark skin, don't be fooled into thinking that you don't need to wear sun protection. Even though you may not burn so easily, you are still vulnerable to sun damage.

> *Note:* Wrinkles caused by sun damage can take up to 15 years to appear.

UVA

The sun's long UVA rays are the ageing rays since they go deep into the skin, destroying its support structure of collagen and elastin (see page 59), causing wrinkles. The intensity of UVA radiation is more constant than UVB without the variations during the day and throughout the year. UVA is just as strong in the winter as in the summer. UVA is also not filtered by glass.

UVB

UVB affects the outer layer of skin, the epidermis, and is the primary agent responsible for sunburns. It is the most intense between the hours of 10 a.m. and 2 p.m. when the sunlight is brightest. It is also more intense in the summer months, accounting for 70 per cent of a person's yearly UVB dose. The shorter UVB rays are cancer-causing because they damage the DNA (genetic information) of cells. The skin itself works really hard to repair any damage, but it is never 100 per cent and skin cancer is caused by the build-up of the left-over residual damage. Unlike UVA, UVB does not penetrate glass.

You *can* get sunburn when it is cloudy. Up to 80 per cent of UVA and UVB rays can penetrate the cloud barrier and can end up causing you more damage because you are less likely to have used sun protection. Infrared rays, which give the feeling of warmth, are filtered more efficiently by clouds, the body therefore doesn't get the signal that it is too hot, so there is a tendency to stay outdoors longer on cloudy days, increasing the risk of burning.

Sunscreens

Sunscreens prevent the free radical damage that is caused by ultraviolet radiation (sunlight). It is important to use a sun cream that protects against both UVA and UVB. While UVB rays cause 80–85 per cent of sunburn, it's UVA that is associated with more long-term skin damage.

> Sun protection factor or SPF: theoretically measures the length of time a that a product can protect the skin from reddening as a result of exposure to UVB radiation, compared to how long the skin takes to redden without protection.

In practice, it isn't advisable to go for more than two hours without reapplying, and it is also important to remember that SPF only works properly if it is applied properly. Most of us only apply a fraction of what we actually should in order to get the full benefit from our sun protection. SPF 15 can block 93 per cent of UVB, and SPF 30 blocks 4 per cent more at 97 per cent, which means that SPF 40s and 50s are packed full of chemicals that aren't necessarily giving as much more protection as we might think.

There are two different kinds of sunscreen:

- *Chemical sunscreens:* absorb UV rays mimicking the action of melanin and account for about 80 per cent of the sunscreen market. A result of how they work means that they convert light radiation to heat and this can lead to some people can getting a heat rash.

> Top Tip: if you are prone to heat rash, don't use a chemical sunscreen with an SPF of higher than 15, because the higher the factor, the more chemicals, the more likely you are to have a reaction.

- *Physical sunscreens:* also known as sun-block, contain micro-reflective particles that act like millions of tiny mirrors reflecting the damaging rays away, include titanium dioxide and zinc oxide. They used to be very white and chalky, but modern ones are much more wearable. If you are prone to sensitive skin, you are better off sticking to a physical sunscreen, and then instead of SPF 15, you can go to SPF 25 if you want to.

You don't have to buy the most expensive sunscreen to know that you are going to be protected. Most budget sunscreen products will protect equally as well as more expensive brands if they contain the right ingredients. A good broad-spectrum sunscreen should have an SPF of at least 15 and contain avobenzone (or Parsol 1789) and titanium dioxide or zinc oxide, which means that it contains both chemical and physical sunscreens. There is more information about the ingredients in sunscreens in the ingredients decoder section (page 105) of Chapter 2.

> *Note:* Sunscreen, kept in a cool place, should last for about a year, definitely no longer than two years. So get rid of all those old bottles of sunscreen that are kicking about in the bottom of the cupboard!

Too much sun exposure will damage your skin, but the sun is also good for us – if we are protected. We need it for the formation of Vitamin D (which reduces the risk of breast, colon, prostate and other cancers), for calcium absorption from the gut (which helps keep bones and teeth healthy and strong) and for balancing hormone levels. The symptoms of certain specific conditions such as eczema and psoriasis may also be helped by exposure to controlled amounts of UV.

The key, as with everything else in our recipe for beauty, is *balance*, so if you are going to go out in the sunshine, just be aware of the dangers and try to be sensible about it.

Tips for more sensible sun bathing

- Avoid sun beds. Even though they don't release UVB, the UVA is so intense that it is a cause of worry for most experts.
- Always wear sunscreen with a minimum SPF 15. Going beyond SPF 15 doesn't really extend the length of time you should stay in the sun in one go without reapplying.
- Apply 30 minutes before you go out in the sun and be aware that a thin layer won't give the protection factor on the bottle – you really need to slather it on.

- Reapply regularly – preferably every hour, but don't wait more than two hours before reapplying.
- Don't sunbathe between 12 p.m. and 2 p.m.
- Eat a diet rich in Vitamins A, C and E (see the section on nutrition, page 24). This will help boost antioxidant levels to fight the free radical damage.
- Be aware that the sun's rays are magnified by altitude, snow and water.
- If you go swimming, try to take a shower immediately afterwards – sea water contains salt, and pool water contains chemicals, both of which are very drying for the skin and leave it more vulnerable to damage from the sun.
- Always reapply sunscreen after swimming – even if it says it's waterproof.
- Applying aftersun lotion can help a little bit to prevent wrinkles and will also help to prevent peeling.
- Suntanned skin needs extra moisturizer in general, as it is more dehydrated.

Fake tanning

Having said all that, the experts seem to unanimously agree that faking it is the only really safe way to tan. Using a self-tanning product can be a great way to lift your mood when it's cold and wintry and you wish you were on holiday. Fake tans contain an active ingredient called *dihydroxyacetone*, otherwise known as DHA. When this comes into contact with the proteins in the outer layers of your skin, it produces a chemical reaction that creates the tan pigment. Even though the skin can become darker, it doesn't mean that you are any more protected from the sun unless your self-tan has SPF in it, and even then you are only protected for the couple of hours after you applied it.

Self-tan comes in several forms: spray, mousse, creams and wipes. Getting it to look natural is the trick. It can take a bit of trial and error, and remember that the more generously you apply, the more intense the result will be. Also, a gradual build-up always works better than an overnight change from pale and mysterious to bronzed beauty. If you do several subtle layers built up over time, the result will be a natural-looking healthy glow.

The best time to apply self-tan is at night, before you go to bed (but make sure it's dry first!), because the tan will have a chance to develop properly overnight and you will have a chance to correct any missed spots in the morning.

My tips for a flawless body fake tan:

1 Exfoliate and moisturize the whole body for three days in a row prior to self-tanning to give the best possible base.

2 Remove any unwanted body hair (legs, underarms, bikini line – see body hair removal, page 52) 24 hours beforehand.

3 Wash, dry and apply moisturizer to whole body, paying special attention to knees, elbows, heels and fingers. Wait ten minutes to allow moisturizer to sink in before applying self-tan.

4 Wear tight-fitting latex gloves, stand in the shower or on an old towel (for easier clean-up afterwards) and apply, starting at toes, working up the body. Apply cream, mousse or lotion and blend using upward strokes everywhere except chest where it works better to use horizontal strokes. If you are using a spray, hold the nozzle about six inches from the skin (slightly farther for hands, feet, inner arms and elbows). Spray upwards from the toes in sweeping motions or small circles.

5 For elbow and knees and back of the ankles, dilute self-tanner by mixing it with a bit of moisturizer to stop the colour collecting in the folds of skin.

6 Also blend the self-tan with moisturizer on paler areas like the neck and inside the arms.

7 For difficult bits like toes: squeeze a walnut-sized blob of self-tanner onto a cotton wool ball and swab over feet, massaging between toes.

8 For hands, you need to take your gloves off and apply a small amount of fake tan to the back of one hand and rub together with the back of the other. Blend thoroughly down the fingers, paying careful attention to the knuckles – the tan can gather in excess skin here if you are not careful.

9 Don't get dressed straight away; you will end up with fake tan all over your clothes and streaks in your tan. Try to wait 15 to 20 minutes before dressing, if you can. It will dry more evenly if you don't come into contact with anything, but if you have to sit down, cover a chair with an old towel, to avoid staining your furniture.

10 Wait four hours before exercising or taking a bath or shower, as sweating makes tan patchy.

11 Some fake tans can be drying so make sure that you use a rich body moisturizer, twice daily, and then your tan should last for three days.

Top Tip: Commonly missed areas are the neck, sides of body and under the breasts.

My tips for a flawless face fake tan:

1 Buy a fake tan that is made especially for the face. It will give a less intense colour and be gentler on the skin. Note that fair skins need only a faint hint of bronze, so go for something with the lowest concentration of DHA. Medium, olive and darker skins can take more.

2 Exfoliate and moisturize your face three days in a row prior to self-tanning to give the best possible base.

3 Pluck eyebrows and remove any other facial hair 24 hours beforehand.

4 Brush your teeth beforehand so that you don't end up with dribble stripes, and if you need to have a drink while your tan is drying, use a straw for the same reason.

5 Cleanse and moisturize your face, allowing ten minutes for moisturizer to sink in. Make sure you avoid lotions that contain *retinol*, *AHAs*, *BHAs* or *glycolic acids*. They are great at exfoliating dead skin cells, but they will also end up taking away your fake tan!

6 Use a barrier cream (something waxy like petroleum jelly or even lip balm) on your hairline and eyebrows to prevent orange patches.

7 Wear tight-fitting latex gloves and squeeze a dollop of product onto your hands and then rub them together to warm the product up.

8 For a subtler tint, mix the fake tan with a bit of moisturizer.

9 Start at the centre of your face; apply a dot of self-tan lotion on the nose, forehead chin and cheeks and blend, sweeping your fingertips outwards and down your neck. Make sure you work it right down to your collarbone and blend it gradually up to your hairline to avoid a tide mark. Dot and blend extra where necessary – never too much at once.

10 Don't forget your eyelids and, if you wear your hair up, remember to do the back of your neck.

11 Use a cotton bud on your eyebrows and hairline to mop up any excess, and use a tissue to lightly dab the creases in the face – crow's feet, smile lines, around the nostrils and just below the lips – where excess tanner can collect.

12 Recreate the sexy wind-burned glow that says 'holiday' rather than 'bottle' by blending a deep shade of cream or gel blusher into the cheeks – in the place where you would naturally get flushed, and a touch of gold or bronze highlighter on top of the cheekbones to make them glow. For more detail, see the section on make-up, page 112.

> Top Tip: Commonly missed areas are the ears – lobes, rims and tops of the ears.

Dealing with streaks:

- Tan corrector wipes are good, or cleansing wipes (preferably the non-alcohol variety), as long as you use them soon after application.
- Darker patches generally mean that you didn't exfoliate well enough beforehand and the fake tan is clinging to build-up of dead skin cells. The best you can do is gently exfoliate over the dark area daily until the colour evens out.
- Light patches: add a bit more tan to the bits you missed.
- As a last resort – a quick once-over with a wedge of lemon will pick up much of the excess colour or some toner on a cotton wool pad should help too.

Hydration *(at least two litres a day)*

Because it makes up two-thirds of our body, and almost half of our brain, water is one of the main factors in the formula for life: The right amount of:

$$water + oxygen + nutrients = healthy \ cells$$
$$= a \ healthy \ body \ and \ good \ skin$$

So basically, hydration = energy, and is absolutely vital for well-being and beauty. If we don't drink enough water, any number of the following things can happen to our bodies:

- Our kidneys won't be able to function; toxins and wastes will build up, leading to all sorts of problems.
- We can get constipated (which can lead to blemish breakouts).
- We are more likely to think that we are hungry all the time, and are therefore prone to eat more.
- It is difficult for the body to use up or metabolise fat stores.
- It is much more difficult for us to regulate our body temperature – we can flip from feeling overheated, to feeling chronically cold and unable to get warm.
- Our brains won't work properly, leading to forgetfulness, lethargy and lack of enthusiasm.
- It is even possible to start losing muscle tone.

If we aren't drinking enough water, not only does it have an effect on our bodies, but also the signs of dehydration will show in the skin before they show anywhere else. In hydrated skin, the cells are properly moist and plumped up so the skin appears softer, more supple and younger. Dehydrated skin cells appear dry, saggy and can be itchy, and are much more prone to disorders and blemishes. The temptation might be to just slather on extra moisturizer, but if we are not keeping hydrated from the inside, any amount of moisturizer on the outside is pretty much useless (because it's not locking any moisture in – there isn't any to lock in!).

The body requires a certain amount of water for efficient circulation, to constantly flush out toxins and keep the cells hydrated. Since the lymphatic system cleans and purifies about two litres of lymph a day, it follows that we need to put two litres of non-toxic fluid (e.g. with no toxins: salt, sugar, caffeine, alcohol or preservatives) into our bodies to make this possible.

> Top Tip: Drinking enough water is an important anti-ageing strategy, because as we get older, our body's water content decreases. So keeping it as hydrated as possible can slow down the ageing process.

Naturally, daily fluid requirements will vary – two litres is for a regular day. Add more if you are drinking coffee, alcohol or fizzy drinks, as they have a diuretic (dehydrating) effect. You will need to add more if you are exercising, or if it's hot and you are perspiring more than normal. If you sit in an air-conditioned or centrally-heated office you will also need to add more. Small sips often are much easier for the body to deal with, than glugging a whole glass down in one.

> Top Tip: Remind yourself to drink water by always having a bottle of filtered or spring water on your desk at work. You can fill it up in the morning and aim to have finished it by the end of the day. If that idea doesn't suit you, then try thinking of it as 'a glass an hour'. This can double not only as an excuse to rest your eyes for a minute (which you should do at least once an hour anyway) but also to stretch your legs for a minute by either walking to the tap or the water cooler. This also helps to boost circulation and can help prevent risk of repetitive strain injuries.
>
> It is also good to have a bottle of water in the car if you are driving for a long period of time, as frequent drinks of water during a long automobile trip can reduce road fatigue.

What is also really good to remember is that sometimes our brains can get confused, and sometimes when we think we are hungry, we are actually thirsty! So, before raiding the snack cupboard, try having a glass of water, because your body may just be asking for a drink instead of food! Also, a glass of water prior to eating can sometimes mean that we don't have to eat as much as we think we need to in order to feel full.

As mentioned above, sugary fizzy drinks, alcohol, caffeinated tea and coffee don't count as fluid intake from a hydration point of view because they are diuretics, which means that they actually flush water *out* of the body. In order to maintain the balance, you need to increase your water intake by one glass for every cup of coffee, glass of wine or fizzy drink. It doesn't just have to be water that you need to drink though – diluted fruit juices and herbal or fruit teas will also do the trick.

It is also possible to boost our fluid intake by increasing the number fluid-rich fruit and vegetables that we eat. The following list of foods all contain at least 90 per cent water: melon, grapefruit, strawberries, broccoli, cabbage, cauliflower, celery, aubergine, lettuce, bell peppers, radish, spinach, courgettes and tomatoes.

> Top Tip: This is very popular with models because it is a great way to hydrate and detox first thing in the morning, getting rid of toxins that take their toll on the skin and getting the day's balancing act off to a positive start: half an hour before breakfast drink a glass of warm water with a slice of lemon or lime. Or just drink a big glass of water in the morning when you wake up – sleep is very dehydrating. This will not only freshen your complexion, it will help to perk you up if you haven't slept well.

Detox *(when necessary)*

If we are following our recipe for beauty and we have all our ingredients in the correct measures, our bodies will function really well: our cells will be busy repairing themselves, our systems will all be working at their optimum performance level and our skin and hair will be looking its best. One of the hardest ingredients to keep in balance is the ingredient of a natural and nutritious wholefood diet. As hard as I might try, I know that I can't resist the odd glass (or three) of wine and I'm afraid that my willpower goes straight out of the window when there is a chocolate mousse within a 20-metere radius – and let's not even get started on Christmas! On top of temptations like these, just living our everyday lives can fill us up with all kinds of toxins; caffeine, alcohol, sugar, fat, environmental pollution, cigarette smoke and chemicals can all accumulate in our bodies, forcing our protection mechanisms to work extra hard to break them down – often resulting in us becoming weak and vulnerable to lethargy and illnesses.

In the same way that I wouldn't want to bake a cake in an already dirty kitchen, I find the best way to start redressing any toxic imbalance in my body, is to detox.

Ways to detox

- Daily detox:
  - Drink two litres of water. It literally flushes the toxins out.
  - Body brushing. It improves circulation and stimulates the lymphatic system in your body so any toxins in your system can be easily dispelled. (Avoid if suffering from broken skin, eczema or psoriasis.) For more details, please see the section on body care in Chapter 2.
- Home detox:
  - Air your home (even in winter!) – getting some fresh air through will help to dilute the toxins from residues from furniture polishes, detergents and air fresheners, etc. that can really build up in the home.
  - Keeping house plants can help to 'clean' the air.
- Evening detox: good after a stressful or toxic day – a hot ginger bath. Grate a thumb sized piece of fresh ginger into a hot (but obviously not too hot) bath. The combination of the heat and the ginger increases circulation while neutralizing the toxins, which are released from the body as sweat. Alternatively, Dead Sea salts are also good for a detox bath.
- Morning detox: good for the morning after and only for the brave – have a contrast shower (three minutes of hot water followed by less than a minute of cold). This increases the circulation, boosts the immune system and kick-starts the removal of toxins from the body.
- Face detox: a great way to detoxify the face – a facial massage. Stimulating the lymphatic system helps to drain impurities out of the face and can immediately improve the appearance of the skin. Please see the section on skin care in Chapter 2 for details of a full facial massage routine.

- Body detox: if your body is feeling really sluggish, any way that gets the circulation moving is a good way to force out a stagnant build-up of toxins in the body. Body brushing is brilliant for this – especially in combination with a food or diet detox. Some exercise, some yoga or even a massage will get everything moving again and you will feel energized and lively again. More information about yoga and exercise is detailed in Chapter 3.

- Food detox: if you listen to your body it will tell you when you have had enough of certain types of food that, in an overload situation, are harder for the body to process than other types of food. Sometimes it's good to just give your body a rest from them. Try having a week break from as many of the following as you think you need to:
  - all dairy products
  - all red meat products
  - refined carbohydrates: cakes, sweets, biscuits, bread, white pasta and breakfast cereals
  - sugars such as sweets, chocolate and table sugar
  - saturated fats (dairy, butter, red meat, all fried foods, mayonnaise, crisps and chips)
  - preservatives, artificial colourings and flavourings
  - any yeast-containing products (including stock cubes)
  - processed/packaged foods
  - alcohol, tea, coffee, soft drinks and fruit juices
  - wheat and wheat-containing products – pasta, bread, biscuits.

  If it's all too difficult and you are stressing out – don't cut things out completely – be reasonable with yourself; just try having less than normal. When re-introducing, try not to undo all the good work with a binge – ease yourself back in gently.

- Diet detox: the following ten-day plan takes a bit more commitment – because it only works properly if you really stick to it. If you do however, it can really help counteract an overloaded system, and can also be very beneficial to the looks. At the end of the ten days, ease yourself gently back into regular meals again. Don't do this too often, and not at all if you are pregnant. If you have any health problems at all, please check with your GP before starting.

– Day 1   drink just water and lemon (hot or cold – but
               not icy)
– Day 2–3   drink fresh fruit juices and herbal teas
– Day 4–7   add vegetables, especially Brussels sprouts,
               broccoli, cauliflower and beetroot, salad leaves
               and fruit
– Day 8–10   add fish, chicken, eggs, garlic, onions, brown
               rice and wheat-free pasta – organic if possible –
               ryvitas, oatcakes, rice cakes and corn cakes,
               and use olive oil to cook with, flaxseed oil on
               salads, and Soya milk products or rice milk
               products (to replace dairy).

For the detox to really work, you also need to make sure that you
have no tea, coffee, alcohol, processed/packaged foods, added
sugar, citrus fruits, spicy foods or yeast-containing products. You
also need to drink at least two litres of water a day.

In order to get the most positive effect from the diet detox you
also need to do a bit of life detox: de-stress by relaxing, maybe
do some yoga have a massage, go for walks, avoid the TV, the
telephone and anything stressful. For yoga and relaxation
techniques, please see the section on yoga in Chapter 3.

Detox side effects

When you are detoxing, the body can often experience some or
all of the following side effects:

• a headache
• more, or smellier, sweat
• fatigue
• feeling unusual emotions
• a dry mouth
• spots, pimples or rashes
• constipation.

These all show that your body is getting rid of toxins. If you
have any concerns at all, make sure you speak to your doctor.

Nutrition *(five portions of fruit and veg a day)*

Like water and oxygen, nutrition is one of the main factors in
the formula for life. The right amount of:

water + oxygen + nutrients = healthy cells
= healthy body and good skin

Food is fuel for the body. The millions of cells that work together to keep us alive all need a constant supply of nutrients in order to function optimally. Just living our day-to-day lives can drain our bodies store of nutrients and vitamins. So in order to keep our bodies healthy and functioning properly we need to eat a diet that is rich in as many of these nutrients and vitamins as possible.

Our fitness, strength, mood, self-image, energy levels, stress levels, brain power, sex drive, sleeping habits and general health can all be affected by what we eat. If our eyes are the windows to our soul, then our skin is the window to our stomach. Our faces are a reflection of what we eat – but not in the way most of us believe. While chips and chocolate won't necessarily give you spots, lack of nutrition will definitely result in an unhealthy complexion – skin that is dull, rough and lifeless. People who eat healthily usually have clear, luminous skin, glossy hair and sparkling eyes. Eating nutritious food nurtures the body. When our bodies are nurtured, we feel good. When we feel good, we smile and when we smile, we look good: we are healthy, happy and therefore more beautiful.

Because a healthy body contributes to healthy skin, it is also important to remember that an unhealthy diet can lead to risks of coronary disease, cancers, fertility problems, obesity, anxiety, behavioural problems, osteoporosis, liver and kidney problems, diabetes and general immunity problems. Also, beware of junk foods such as cakes, biscuits, ready meals and anything that contains hydrogenated vegetable oils (trans fats), sweeteners, colourings or additives as these foods hinder the body's natural digestive processes leading to poor circulation. The resulting build-up of wastes and toxins is how cellulite can start.

A healthy diet is not a 'diet' or a quick fix, it is really a healthful balanced eating plan for life, and the key to making it work is to be realistic and not fanatical – as with everything it is all about getting the balance right. The minute we get fanatical, we are dealing with deprivation, which is the mother of failure. A healthy eating plan is just that – a plan to make the things that you eat, and the way that you eat them, healthier. It isn't necessarily a weight-loss programme, although, if you stick to the plan (and combine it with some exercise), any excess weight will come off gradually, and if you continue to eat healthily, it will stay off.

Be realistic though and try not to wind yourself up into a guilt-ridden frenzy for not sticking 100 per cent to the plan. The stress that you give yourself might do you more damage than an occasional bar of chocolate or packet of crisps, especially if you end up comfort eating to drown out the guilt. If you are generally eating healthily, the odd treat isn't going to do you any harm. Keeping the balance can be easier than you think: if you stray off track one day, you just need to balance the next day with a day of eating and drinking as healthily as possible. It is important not to set ourselves unrealistic goals in the first place and to realize that the best way to achieve anything is slowly and steadily – a bit less food here, a bit more exercise there, nothing too radical. This way the change is neither a shock to the body nor to the mind, and therefore something that is quite maintainable in the long term.

It is also important to remember that if your body is to benefit properly from all these nutrients, then our digestive system also needs to be in tip-top condition. This, just like our recipe for beauty, is achieved by a combination of good posture, good breathing, exercise, lack of stress, drinking enough water and getting enough sleep. Another way to give the digestive system a boost is to chew our food more before swallowing. Hopefully all this information can be a way to help you to be aware of what is out there and what you can do to balance the ingredients in your beauty 'cake' – remember, a healthy body is one of the ingredients, so is healthy skin – these can both be improved with a more nutritious diet and eating plan.

Healthy eating plan

- Breakfast is vital. Eating first thing in the morning helps to stabilize blood sugar levels, which then regulate appetite and energy. A good breakfast means that you are less likely to be hungry during the rest of the day and are, therefore, less likely to overeat.
- Drink lots of water – at least two litres – for general hydration, to detoxify and to aid the digestive system. For more information on the benefits of drinking water, please see the section on hydration in Chapter 1.
- Eat five portions of fresh fruit or vegetables a day, a portion being:
  - one piece of medium-sized fruit – e.g. an apple, peach, banana or orange
  - one slice of large fruit, such as melon, mango or pineapple
  - one handful of grapes or two handfuls of cherries or berry fruits.

- one tablespoon of dried fruit
- a glass (roughly 100 ml) of fruit or vegetable juice
- a side salad
- a serving (roughly 100 g) of vegetables – e.g. frozen or mushy peas, boiled carrots or stir-fried broccoli.

Top Tip: If you can't get through five servings of fruit and vegetables in a day, then try juicing several fruits each morning for a healthy breakfast drink – a great start to the day.

- Try to include more whole (i.e. not refined or processed) organic and fresh foods in your diet, and try to avoid hydrogenated fats, burned food and reduce your intake of saturated fats from meat, dairy produce and junk food.
- Try to eat fish three times a week.
- Use cold-pressed seed oils on salad dressings; get your daily-recommended serving of seeds by sprinkling them on top of your salad.
- Cook food lightly and simply: steam, microwave, grill, poach, braise, roast, stir-fry or cook 'en papillotte' (wrapped in foil and baked in the oven). This not only keeps the majority of the nutrients in the food, but also cuts the need for too much excess oil.
- Make eating an experience for all the senses. The body and the brain will derive not only more satisfaction from the experience, but also more value – both physically and mentally. Don't treat eating food as a means to an end, treat it as an experience to be enjoyed – and it will be! Eat at the table, present the food nicely, take the time to really enjoy your food – smelling and savouring it. If your senses are satisfied, it follows that your stomach will also feel more satisfied.
- Also, if you eat so quickly that you are practically inhaling your food, sometimes the message from your brain to say that you are full gets sent out, but you have been eating so quickly that you have shovelled in another half a plateful that your body didn't even need. Eating slowly, and chewing properly means that you are more likely to be aware when you are actually full and not over-fill yourself.
- Chewing your food properly also means that the digestive system can do it's job properly which means that you don't end up with loads of undigested food in your system (food that was too big to be broken down in the stomach). This can

lead to all kinds of digestive problems. Not only that, but if the food remains undigested then the body can't properly absorb the nutrients which means you also run the risk of your immune system not being able to function properly.

- Try to have desserts and naughty snacks less often and in smaller portions. Help this along by not filling your cupboards with temptation. Try to stock up on healthy snacks – for some snack ideas, see the section on savvy snacking, page 37.

Top Tip: I used to be a two to three bar a day chocoholic. Now I just have two or three squares of a good quality dark chocolate as my after dinner treat. The high percentage of cocoa solids and low amount of sugar means that I get my chocolate fix without craving loads more.

- Less is more – go for quality of food not quantity.
- Everything in moderation – don't deprive yourself, teach yourself that a small amount, savoured and enjoyed, really is enough. You don't have to be greedy.
- Try to eat the widest possible variety of foods with high nutritional value: the following table lists a selection of foods that when eaten as the major part of a balanced diet, have many benefits, not only for health, but for the skin and for beauty as well.

Note: to get the most benefit from the 'anti-cellulite' foods, you also need to drink even more water than the recommended two litres, limit your salt intake and completely cut out chocolate, sweets, crisps, alcohol and processed foods.

- Don't make any dramatic change to your diet without first consulting your doctor.

Table of healthy foods and their nutrient content

	Protect skin (anti-oxidants)	Regenerate skin and anti-ageing	Rehydrate skin	Anti-cellulite	General health
Apples	Vit C	Vit C + lecithin	High water content	Gentle laxative and diuretic effect	Vit C, potassium + fibre
Apricots	Vit A (beta carotene)		High water content		Vit A (beta carotene)
Artichoke		Silica			
Asparagus	Vit C + glutathione	Vit C + silica			Vit C + glutathione
Avocados	Glutathione, oleic acid	Vit E	Fatty acids + high water content	Fatty acids + vitamin E	Potassium, glutathione, oleic acid
Banana	Vit C	Vit B6 + B12	High water content		Vit C, Vit B6 + B12 + potassium + fibre
Bell peppers	Vit C	Vit B6 + B12 + silica	High water content	Vit C	Vit C, Vit B6 + B12
Beetroot		Silica			Iron
Berries	Vit C + polyphenols	Vit C	High water content	Vit C + polyphenols	Vit C + polyphenols
Brazil nuts	Vit E + selenium				Vit E + selenium
Broccoli	Vit C, glutathione, beta carotene, lutein, quercetin, selenium + coenzyme Q10	Vit C + iron	High water content	Vit C, glutathione, beta carotene, lutein, quercetin + fibre	Vit C, glutathione, beta carotene, lutein, quercetin, selenium, coenzyme Q10, iron, chromium + fibre
Brown rice	Selenium	Vit B6 + B12, magnesium + silica			Vit B6 + B12, selenium + magnesium

Brussels sprouts	Vit C	Vit C			Vit C
Cabbage	Vit C	Vit C, Vit B6 + B12			Vit C, Vit B6 + B12
Carrots	Vit A (beta carotene)		High water content	Vit A (beta carotene)	Vit A (beta carotene)
Cauliflower	Vit C	Vit C + lecithin	High water content		Vit C
Chick peas		Calcium + lignan			Calcium
Chillies and hot peppers					Capsicum
Citrus fruits	Vit C	Vit C		Vit C	Vit C + potassium
Cranberries	Polyphenols		High water content	Polyphenols	Polyphenols
Cucumber			High water content		
Dairy	Vit A (retinol) + zinc	Calcium, Vit A (retinol), Vit B6 + B12			Vit A (retinol), Vit B6 + B12, calcium, zinc + Vit D
Eggs	Vit E + selenium	Zinc, lecithin, sulphur + protein amino acids		Protein amino acids	Vit E, selenium + sulphur
Fennel		Silica		Detox properties	
Fish and fish oils	Selenium, glutathione + coenzyme Q10	Calcium, Vit B6 + B12, omega 3 fatty acids + protein amino acids	Omega 3 fatty acids	Omega 3 + 6 fatty acids + protein amino acids	Calcium Vit B6, B12 + Vit D, omega 3 fatty acids, potassium, selenium, glutathione + coenzyme Q10
Garlic					Allicin
Grapefruit	Vit C + ferulic acid	Vit C + ferulic acid	High water content	Vit C	Vit C + ferulic acid
Kale	Vit A (beta carotene) + lutein				Vit A (beta carotene) + lutein

Kiwi fruit	Vit C	Vit C	High water content	Vit C	Vit C
Leafy greens	Vit C, Vit E + manganese			Vit C	Vit C, Vit E + manganese
Lemon	Vit C	Vit C	High water content	Vit C	Vit C + natural antiseptic
Liver	Vit A (retinol)	Vit A (retinol)			Vit A (retinol)
Melon (cantaloupe + honeydew)	Vit A (beta carotene)		High water content		Vit A (beta carotene) + potassium
Muesli	Vit E	Vit E			Vit E
Mushrooms		Zinc			
Nuts	Vit E, selenium, copper, manganese + zinc	Magnesium, iron + fatty acids	Fatty acids	Omega 3 + 6 fatty acids + Vit E	Vit E, selenium, copper, manganese, zinc, magnesium, iron + B vitamins
Oats		Beta-glucan, Vit E + silicic acid		Beta-glucan, Vit E + silicic acid	Slow-release energy, beta-glucan, Vit E + silicic acid
Olive oil	Vit E + oleic acid				Vit E + oleic acids
Onions	Quercetin + selenium	Silica	High water content		Quercetin + selenium
Orange	Vit C + Vit A (beta carotene)	Vit C	High water content	Vit C	Vit C + Vit B (beta carotene)
Pink grapefruit	Vit C + lycopene		High water content	Vit C	Vit C + lycopene
Pineapple	Manganese		High water content		Manganese + bromelain
Plums	Ferulic acid		High water content		
Potatoes	Vit C	Vit C			Potassium
Protein (lean red meat, chicken, turkey)	Glutathione	Protein amino acids + sulphur		Protein amino acids	Glutathione, potassium, protein + sulphur

Pulses (beans, lentils)	Copper, zinc	Magnesium, iron, lignan			Iron, copper, zinc
Pumpkin	Vit A (beta carotene)				Vit A (beta carotene)
Red grapes	Quercetin		High water content		Quercetin
Red meat	Zinc	Iron, zinc, Vit B6 + B12			Iron, zinc, Vit B6 + B12
Red wine (one glass)	Polyphenols				Polyphenols
Salad leaves			High water content		High water content + fibre
Seeds and seed oils	Vit E, selenium, copper + manganese	Omega 3 + 6 fatty acids, zinc	Omega 3 + 6 fatty acids	Omega 3 + 6 fatty acids	Vit E, selenium, copper + manganese
Shellfish	Selenium	Iron			Selenium + iron
Spinach	Vit C, Vit A (beta carotene), lutein + coenzyme Q10	Vit C + lecithin	High water content	Vit C, Vit A (beta carotene), lutein, coenzyme Q10 + Vit K	Vit C, Vit A (beta carotene), lutein, coenzyme Q10, iron, vitamin K + fibre
Strawberries	Vit C + ferulic acid		High water content	Vit C	Vit C
Sweetcorn	Ferulic acid				
Sweet potatoes	Vit E, Vit C + Vit A (beta carotene)	Vit C			Vit E, Vit C + Vit A (beta carotene)
Tea (green or black)	Flavinoids				Flavinoids
Tomatoes	Vit C, lycopene + selenium	Vit C	High water content	Vit C, lycopene + selenium	Vit C, lycopene, potassium + selenium
Tofu (soy bean curd)		Vit B6 + B12, calcium, flavones, lecithin + protein amino acids		Protein amino acids	B vits, calcium + protein amino acids
Tuna (fresh)	Selenium				Selenium

Watermelon	Lycopene + glutathione		High water content		Lycopene + glutathione
Wheat germ	Vit E, selenium, manganese + coenzyme Q10				Vit E, selenium, manganese + coenzyme Q10
Whole grains	Zinc, ferulic acid + coenzyme Q10	Vit B6 + B12, zinc, iron + magnesium			Iron, Vit B6 + B12, zinc + coenzyme Q10

These nutrients are explained in more detail in the appendix: Nutrients, Chapter 6. This is only a basic list. A nutrition specialist will be able to provide you with much more information if you are interested.

> Top Tip: If you suffer from PMS, a wholefood diet, high in fibre, vegetables, fruit and water will help balance hormones and can be a very effective way to manage PMS. Keeping blood sugar levels stable is also important as refined foods, high-sugar diets and caffeine can aggravate the symptoms.

Things to be aware of (good stuff)

- Bananas contain lots of potassium and natural sugar. This releases much more slowly into the body than refined sugar. This makes a banana a much 'better' sugary snack than a bar of chocolate.
- Brazil nuts are very high in the antioxidant minerals selenium and vitamin E.
- Cranberries are a natural diuretic, which means that they help to flush out toxins. They are often used to help treat cystitis.
- Garlic is a good natural cold medication. It acts as a decongestant, expectorant and anti-inflammatory agent.
- Isoflavones (Soya and Tofu) can help to reduce menopausal symptoms including mood swings and hot flushes.
- Eating protein at every meal is an important anti-ageing strategy because it helps to repair and strengthen cell structure and stimulate the production of collagen and elastin which keeps the skin supple. For more information on collagen and elastin, please see the section on skin care in Chapter 2.

- Silica or silicic acid (artichoke, asparagus, beetroot, bell peppers, oats and brown rice) is good for helping to minimize the appearance of lines and wrinkles and keeping skin looking plump and youthful.
- Vitamin K (found in turnip greens, liver, broccoli, cabbage, cauliflower, lettuce, Soya, spinach) helps to improve blood flow to cellulite-affected areas, and a lack of it can sometimes be the cause of dark circles under the eyes.
- Yoghurt (live – with acidphilus) is vitamin-rich and nutritious. Because it maintains the levels of good bacteria in the gut, it can boost your immune system, prevent yeast infections and stop bad breath. Particularly good to eat if you are taking antibiotics which can upset these levels.

Top Tip: Frozen yoghurt is a great substitute for ice cream as a dessert.

Things to be aware of (not so good stuff)

- Alcohol is very toxic to the body and puts a real strain on the digestive system and the liver.
- Caffeine is a natural diuretic – it forces the body to flush liquid out of its system, and is therefore dehydrating. It is a stimulant drug, so excess can lead to high blood pressure. It also reduces the absorption of iron and zinc, which affects the immune system, and can mean that you get sick very easily if you drink a lot of it. Also, drinking coffee within one hour of a meal can reduce the body's iron absorption by up to 80 per cent.
- Not enough calcium can lead to: osteoporosis (weak and brittle bones), insomnia, premenstrual cramps and hypertension (high blood pressure).
- Dairy products while being a good source of calcium and protein can be tough on the digestive system when consumed in excess. Avoid if you suffer from allergies and/or spots.
- Not enough fatty acids (oily fish, nuts, grains and seeds and canola, linseed/flaxseed, sunflower and evening primrose oil) in the diet will lead to dry skin.
- Fruits are high in good antioxidant vitamins, but they are also highly acidic, so don't eat too much at once, especially if you are having problems with your skin.
- Iodine rich foods (eggs, malted breads, shellfish), eaten in large quantities, can sometimes trigger an acne-like reaction in the skin.

- Processed foods (ready meals and fast foods) have little nutritional value and are full of additives and preservatives that can do our bodies more harm than good, some of which even cause free radical damage.
- Saturated fats (butter, margarine, fatty meat, cheese) will damage tissue walls and reduce circulation; a diet high in saturated fat and high in salt is associated with an increased risk of coronary heart disease.
- Simple carbohydrates are found in refined flour and sugar (cakes, biscuits, sweets and regular pasta). The refining process removes the majority of vitamins and minerals from these foods. The body treats them as though they were pure sugars, and the excess residues are stored as fat in the body.
- Sugar (in excess) is not only detrimental to overall health, but it will also have a negative impact on your skin. Sugar attaches to protein molecules in the skin and changes their action, impacting on the collagen and elastin production (collagen and elastin are explained in detail in the section on skin care in Chapter 2.)
- Trans fats (hydrogenated vegetable oils) found in many processed foods, cakes, biscuits and chocolate contain constituents that form free radicals. They also clog up and slow circulation and also stop the body from being able to utilize the good fats properly. They lurk in hydrogenated oils and margarines, biscuits and chips – just 20g a day can add years to your biological age.
- Wheat and dairy products (in excess) can sometimes lead to symptoms of bloatedness, tiredness and headaches. Wheat contains gluten, which lines the intestines and can delay the absorption of nutrients in the digestive tract. Dairy often has a similar effect on the respiratory tract.
- Smokers and women taking the contraceptive pill are generally depleted of vitamin E and will need to increase their intake either from food (nuts, seeds, green leafy vegetables, broccoli, cereals, oats, grains, eggs, olive oil) or in supplement form in order to maintain the best possible health and therefore beauty.
- Yeasts, used as a raising agent in most baked foods and found also in many packaged foods, fermented foods (vinegar, soy sauce and cheese) and alcoholic drinks (especially beer and wine), can be very problematic for people who suffer from yeast infections allergies, asthma, eczema and migraine.
- Not enough zinc can often be the cause of white spots on the fingernails and certain skin conditions.

Alternative healthy recipe ideas

Grilled salmon with orange glaze

Why it's good for you: high omega-3 fat in salmon; antioxidants in orange rind, spring onions and garlic; ginger very good for the stomach.

Ingredients (serves 4):

- 2 tablespoons orange marmalade
- 2 teaspoons sesame oil
- 2 teaspoons reduced-sodium soy sauce
- ½ teaspoon grated fresh ginger root
- 1 garlic clove, crushed
- 3 tablespoons white rice vinegar (or other white vinegar)
- 1 lb (450g) boneless, skinless salmon fillet, cut in four pieces
- 6 spring onions, thinly sliced with green (optional)
- 1 tablespoon toasted sesame seeds (optional)

Directions:

Combine marmalade, oil, soy sauce, ginger, garlic and vinegar. Heat grill. Brush glaze on each side of salmon; grill for about five minutes on each side. Top with spring onions and sesame seeds and serve.

Pizza tricolore (three colours)

Why it's good for you: powerful antioxidants in peppers, onion, garlic and herbs; vegetables can help lower high blood pressure.

Ingredients (serves 4–6):

- 1 (30 cm, 12 inch) thin pizza crust (homemade or from the shop)
- 1 red bell pepper, chopped
- 1 green bell pepper, chopped
- 1 yellow bell pepper, chopped
- 1 sliced red or yellow onion, pulled into rings
- 3 cloves garlic, crushed
- 2 tablespoons extra-virgin olive oil
- 1½ teaspoons dried Italian herbs
- Crushed red pepper flakes, to taste (optional)
- Crumbled feta cheese, to taste

Directions:

Preheat oven to 230 degrees, gas mark 8. Lay crust on pizza pan or cookie sheet. In a bowl, combine remaining ingredients except cheese; spoon over crust. Top with cheese. Bake 10–12 minutes, or until vegetables are crispy-tender.

Lemon berry yoghurt

Why it's good for you: low saturated fat; high antioxidants; all the good bacteria in the yoghurt.

Ingredients (Serves 4):

- 300–350g (12oz) fresh or thawed frozen berries (whichever sort you fancy)
- 500g (18oz) natural yoghurt
- the zest of one lemon (unwaxed)

Directions:

Mix together all the ingredients in a bowl and then serve in four glasses (wineglasses are nice for a dinner party).

Savvy snacking

Instead of viewing snacks as naughty treats, try to think about them as mini-meals, and use them as a way to not only gain extra nutrition, but to also make your main meals smaller. By eating smaller meals and snacking often, you will naturally increase your resting metabolic rate – meaning that your body will naturally burn more calories. In an effort to diet and lose weight, many people eat just one meal a day, which is about the worst thing you can do for your body, and its metabolism. When you only feed your body once or twice in a 24-hour period, your body tries its hardest to hold on to the food you eat – storing as much of the fat as it can, and slowing down its resting metabolic rate at the same time. Whereas, if you eat small meals often, your body knows that within an hour or two, it'll be getting more fuel and food, so it doesn't hesitate to use whatever you just fed it. Also over time, this will increase your body's resting metabolic rate – increasing your natural fat-burning.

My favourite between-meal snacks

- a handful of dried fruits and nuts
- 2 rye crispbreads with a spoonful of guacamole
- a strawberry and banana smoothie
- a handful of Japanese rice crackers
- vegetable crudités and a tomato salsa dip

- a small spinach salad sprinkled with seeds
- 110g low fat Greek yoghurt with a spoonful of honey and a sprinkling of either toasted oats or almonds
- a handful of mixed berries
- an apple or a banana.

Top Tip: Eat a protein snack before you go out to a party. First, it will stave off hunger and stop you from eating all the canapés. Second, if you are going to drink alcohol, it will prevent you from getting drunk too quickly as alcohol doesn't get absorbed into the bloodstream as quickly if there is food already in the stomach.

Protein packed snacks:

Half an avocado with a few prawns

Vegetable sticks with hummus

A piece of leftover roast chicken

A boiled egg

A small piece of smoked fish (salmon, mackerel)

A portion of low fat natural or Greek yoghurt

A handful of nuts.

Sleep *(8 hours)*

The better we sleep, the better we look and the better we feel. Most of us know this, but never get around to changing our habits. We know that in order to get a good eight hours we need to be asleep by a certain time, but either we don't feel tired enough at that time, or something good is on the television, and there goes another hour or two that would be better spent sleeping.

Many of us will try to argue that we do just fine thanks on six or seven hours, but the scientists say that the reason that we need eight hours is that between the seventh and eighth hour is when we get almost an hour of rapid eye movement (REM) sleep. It is during REM when all the 'action' (see below) happens. REM sleep occurs about every 90 minutes, and the periods of REM sleep get longer as the night progresses. So, if you're a six-hour sleeper, you're missing that last, and longest, opportunity to repair and to prepare for the coming day.

During REM sleep

- Hormones are released and the body goes into repair mode and regenerates skin, blood and brain cells, as well as muscles. They don't call it beauty sleep for nothing! You can drink water and watch your diet, but without sleep you won't have glowing skin.
- Our brains process information – anything that we have learned during the day, this is when it sinks in. So if you've got an exam, getting a good night's sleep could prove more fruitful than staying up several nights and cramming because you need the sleep for your brain to absorb the information properly.
- Our immune system gets a boost.
- Fat stores are broken down and blood sugar is normalized.

Lack of sleep in general can result in:

- Depleted looks – dull and lifeless skin, dark circles under the eyes
- Increased arterial ageing, increasing the risk of heart attacks
- Low immunity and vulnerability to infections
- Weight gain – insufficient sleep means that the brain releases less *serotonin*, which often results in the body craving sweet and fatty foods as a temporary boost, which only serve to pile on the pounds
- Reduced concentration – you are more likely to make mistakes and have a slower reaction time
- Cranky, aggressive and anti-social behaviour. Taken to extremes, severe sleep deprivation causes disorientation and paranoia.

Top tips for a good night's sleep

- Don't bring work stress home with you. Leave it at work to be dealt with the next day. Trying to do work at home, or trying to resolve work issues during the evening can trigger a stress response that will make it difficult to get a good night's sleep. For more information about stress and the stress response, please refer to the next section, on stress.
- Keep the bedroom as a restful sanctuary; don't fill it up with radiation-emitting gadgets like TVs, computers and games consoles.
- Try to get a little bit of exercise in the daytime before 6 p.m., so that you don't get a temporary boost in your metabolism that might make it hard to sleep.

- Try to get into a routine of going to bed at the same time, and getting up at the same time.
- Don't eat your evening meal too close to bedtime (three hours before is preferable) and if possible, make it light and easy to digest. Try to get into the habit of making lunch – or even breakfast – your main meal.
- Avoid alcohol, caffeine, sweet puddings, hot sugary drinks and cigarettes at bedtime as all these things stimulate the brain.
- Don't have a hot bath before bed – it dilates the blood vessels stimulating the mind and body.
- Don't lie awake fretting. If you are worried about something, write it down on a piece of paper and then put it on the bedside table so that you can forget about it and come back to it in the morning with a clear head.
- Drink some water before sleeping and have a glass next to the bed – dehydration forces the pulse rate up = anxiety = disturbed sleep.
- Wind down before bed – massage is great for this! So are relaxation exercises. Try some of the relaxation exercises detailed in the section on yoga, Chapter 3.
- Closing the curtains will keep out distracting lights, or for even more darkness, wear an eye mask.
- If noise bothers you (especially snoring partners) try sleeping with earplugs in.

Failing all that, if you still don't get a good night's sleep, and you are having a rotten day, take a nap – it may be one of the best things you can do to correct poor mental performance and self-confidence. Most people's bodies naturally become more tired in the afternoon, about eight hours after we wake up. Don't nap for too long though as you may end up disturbing your next night's sleep, and 20 minutes is all we need to feel refreshed and lively again.

Top Tip: Sleeping on your back with your head slightly elevated (either by one supportive pillow or two softer ones) is a great way to prevent puffy eyes and wrinkles on the sides of the face.

Stress *(minimum)*

Stress affects every single ingredient in our recipe for beauty so if we want to really maximize our beauty potential, we need to seriously look at regulating our stress levels. Stress can manifest itself both physically and mentally. If you often find yourself feeling any of the following, then you are most likely suffering from some form of stress:

Physically:
- heart palpitations
- short breathing
- stomach problems
- muscle tension, aches and pains
- tight jaw/teeth grinding
- clenched fists
- restlessness and impatience
- sleep problems: either not enough or constant lethargy
- low immunity – constant colds, headaches
- hot/cold flushes
- appetite issues: too much or not enough
- increased interest in alcohol
- loss of libido.

Mentally:
- feelings of anxiety or depression
- feelings of confusion
- feeling out of control
- being forgetful
- having up and down moods and emotions
- being easily aggravated
- feelings of frustration
- having low self-esteem
- procrastinating
- lacking concentration
- being accident prone
- feeling overwhelmed
- feeling tearful.

The main problem with stress is the way that the human body responds to it. It does it the same way now as it did millions of years ago. Even though modern day stresses are more likely to be financial worries, work pressures, traffic jams or rows at home, the body still responds the same way as if an angry lion was chasing us. Its protection mechanism, or the 'fight or flight' response, kicks in. The brain gets a signal that there is something stressful happening and it releases hormones into the blood stream:

- *Cortisol* (to release glucose into the blood stream for energy)
- *Adrenaline* (to make our hearts beat faster)
- *Noradrenaline* (to help us run faster and fight harder – sending all the blood to our hands and feet and tensing muscles in preparation for running or fighting).

In order to concentrate blood and energy on what it thinks is actually a 'fight or flight' task, these hormones also shut down some of our bodily functions that are considered to be 'non-essential' in times of life or death: mainly the immune system and the digestive system. Once in a while, this won't affect us too badly, but if we are often in stressful situations, we could not only be more susceptible to cold sores, coughs, sniffles and minor aches and pains, but weakened immune systems also encourage more serious conditions such as heart disease, infertility, strokes and diabetes. If the digestive system is shut down for too long we can get symptoms of queasiness, bloating, wind and stomach upsets. Food can ferment and stagnate in the large intestines leading to diarrhoea and constipation. Prolonged amounts of acid in the stomach can lead to indigestion and ulcers.

Stress affects our skin both directly and indirectly. Indirectly it affects our skin because our skin reflects what is going on inside our bodies. When we are stressed our appearance is strained and pinched, we have dull eyes, hunched shoulders and a taut body. Worry manifests itself in the skin as dryness, dullness, frown lines and wrinkles. When the body releases excess adrenaline, it also releases more androgen hormones, and these trigger the skin to over-produce sebum (oil), which can lead to spots and blemishes.

Stress affects our sleep, because when we are stressed the brain doesn't release enough *serotonin* and *melatonin*, (the hormones that regulate the body's natural 24-hour sleep cycle). Without enough of these, we don't get enough sleep. We might find it hard to fall asleep and may wake frequently during the night. We might have vivid dreams and often won't feel rested in the morning. Too much cortisol is also a problem because it causes a heightened state of alertness and arousal (it's basically a 'sugar rush') making a restful night's sleep almost impossible.

Stress also affects our mood. Low self-esteem, irritability, guilt, pessimism, procrastination and general grouchiness are all short-term stress signals. They are very easy to ignore, because we all have our ups and downs – but if left unchecked these feelings can spiral. Depression, anxiety, panic attacks and other mood disorders can result.

In *Teach Yourself Managing Stress* by Terry Looker and Olga Gregson, stress is defined as 'a state we experience when there is a mismatch between perceived demands and perceived ability to cope'. They go on to say that 'to get the right balance we need to reappraise how we perceive and interact with our environment because this determines the way we match up our demands with our ability to cope'.

In other words: in order to reduce stress in our lives, we need to look at the balance between what is demanded of us in our lives and how we cope with these demands. Then we need to find ways to reduce the amount of demands and increase our coping resources.

In the long term, 'stress management' is something that most of us need to factor into our daily lives, and *Teach Yourself Managing Stress* is a great step-by-step guide packed with all the information and advice needed to do that. In the short term, there are many ways to combat the negative effects of stress in our lives.

Things that can relieve stress in the short term

• *Acupressure* Visiting a qualified therapist for a session of acupressure can do a lot to help relieve the symptoms of stress. But there are some small things that you can do for yourself. When you feel like everything is starting to overwhelm you, try holding your frontal eminences (see Figure 1.1) – while you do so, think about the stressful event that is bothering you – gradually you should find that the stress lessens. The frontal eminences are reflex points with connections to the central meridian (involved with the brain), the stomach meridian and the bladder meridian, and by applying pressure here, you will send calming messages, which reverse the stress response, and disperse the gathering black clouds.

figure 1.1 frontal eminences

- *Reiki* A reiki therapist can help to ease the symptoms of stress-related conditions by channelling 'ki', or life energy, into the patient to rebalance and replenish areas where it is depleted. In theory, reiki acts on an atomic level, causing the body's molecules to vibrate with higher intensity and thus dissolving energy blockages that can lead to disharmony and disease.

- *Reflexology* A reflexologist can help to relieve the symptoms of stress by utilizing the principle that there are reflexes in the feet, which correspond to every organ and system in the body. Stimulating particular nerve impulses is said to improve the body's natural healing mechanism.

- *Massage* A massage therapist can help to relieve the symptoms of stress by using a variety of hand movements to manipulate the soft tissues of the body for the purpose of normalizing them. The basic goal is to help the body heal itself and to increase health and well-being.

- *Have a quick stretch* This quick stretch is handy for reducing stress levels: lock your hands loosely behind your head and gently pull down so your face moves towards your chest (see Figure 1.2). Hold for 15 seconds breathing deeply and evenly.

figure 1.2 quick stretch

- *Breathe* A few moments of controlled breathing is great for calming us down when we feel like we are about to boil over. For some breathing exercises, please see the section on yoga in Chapter 3.
- *Go for a walk* If you are feeling low, take 20 minutes and go outside for a walk, preferably somewhere green. Not only will the surroundings boost your mood, but also the light physical exercise will improve production of serotonin, one of the brain's so-called 'happy hormones'.
- *Exercise* By doing some exercise you use up the excess adrenaline caused by stress, and the body feels like it has either 'fought' or 'fled' and therefore the stress response dissipates. For some exercise ideas, please see the section on exercise in Chapter 3.
- *Yoga* Holding yoga postures while controlling your breathing calms both the body and the mind. It also uses up some of the adrenaline by working the muscles, and the relaxation techniques rebalance the stress levels in the body and mind. For some more information about yoga, please see Chapter 3.

- *Have a laugh* Phone a funny friend or rent a funny movie. Laughter lowers stress hormones while at the same time boosting the body's natural antibodies and immune response and increases the oxygen supply in the blood.
- *Have a cuddle* Have a tactile experience, stroke your cat or dog, or have a cuddle with your partner: touch has remarkable healing qualities, it can lower your heart rate and increase the release of 'feel-good' *endorphins* in the brain.
- *Plan a girl's night* Studies prove that a night out with the girls ups the body's stores of *oxytocin* – another one of the brain's happy hormones, which acts as a stress reliever.
- *Eat well* When the body is under stress it needs an extra dose of B vitamins, as they are responsible for the smooth running of the nervous system. Good sources of vitamin B are: liver, meat, brown rice, fish, butter, wheat germ, whole grain cereals and soybeans. Vitamin C is also good for tackling the effects of stress on the body. Good sources of vitamin C are: berries, kiwi fruit, citrus fruit, broccoli, cauliflower, Brussels sprouts, cabbage, green leafy vegetables and bell peppers. Oily fish such as salmon, sardines and mackerel are also good because they contain essential fatty acids, which help to block production of the enzymes that make us feel tense when under pressure.

Top Tip: Avoid high sugar snacks when stressed. Most of us crave carbohydrates when we are feeling down, but heavily processed sweets send a spike of sugar into the blood stream, and although we might feel better immediately, swings in blood sugar levels can lead to anxiety, irritability, headaches, confusion – basically leaving us worse off than we were before! Avoid anything made with refined white sugar or flour (cakes, biscuits, white bread or pasta). The best things to have are foods that are high in calcium or magnesium as these can be calming (nuts, seeds, yoghurt). But if it HAS to be something sweet, then have a piece of fruit instead.

Feel-good easy snack fruits:

apples

pears

bananas

figs

dates.

02

icing the cake: refining your beautiful face and body

In this chapter you will learn:
- how your skin works
- how to look after your skin and body at different stages of your life
- how to identify the right products for your skin and body
- how to best apply different kinds of make up to create your own customized look.

Body care *(body brush and moisturize daily)*

All the things mentioned in the previous chapter like diet, hydration, exercise, posture, yoga and relaxation, are all important factors in keeping our bodies fit, healthy and revitalized from the inside. We mustn't forget that we have a layer of skin on the outside that also needs to be cared for, maybe not in quite so much detail as our faces, but cared for nonetheless. Regular exfoliation and using moisturizer daily are the best things that we can do to keep the skin on our body in tip-top condition. In this chapter I hope to explain why and how, and also give some advice about ways to remove unwanted body hair.

Body brushing

Body brushing, also known as 'dry skin brushing' is a very simple and effective way of helping our bodies to get rid of toxins while at the same time making our skin glow. There are millions of sweat ducts all over our skin, and the skin gets rid of quite a lot of toxins through our sweat. The skin is actually responsible for one quarter of the body's detoxification each day. It is an extremely vital part of our immune system and it is our first line of defence against disease and illness! So, taking care of it and helping it to get rid of those toxins is a great way not only to maintain healthy skin and a healthy body but it is also another way to balance the ingredients for our beauty cake.

The benefits of body brushing:

- It rejuvenates the nervous system by stimulating nerve endings in the skin.
- It helps with muscle tone and aids a more even distribution of fat deposits.
- It helps to shed dead skin cells, which improves the texture of the skin and encourages cell renewal, and therefore improves the appearance and moisture-retaining qualities of the skin.
- It helps your skin to absorb nutrients by de-clogging pores. Healthy, breathing skin contributes to overall body health.
- It increases circulation to the skin, encouraging the body to discharge waste, which greatly aids the lymphatic drainage of the entire body. When the body rids itself of toxins, it is able to run more efficiently in all areas. The workings of the lymphatic system are explained in more detail in Chapter 1 in the section on balancing the ingredients, page 4.

- It also helps to tighten the skin because it increases the flow of blood. This can help to lessen the appearance of cellulite, especially if your diet gets better at the same time.

Cellulite is basically a build-up of toxic materials that haven't been eliminated and have accumulated in the body's fat cells. The best way to prevent it, is to make sure that we get rid of as much of our toxic waste as possible. In combination with a nutritious healthy diet and some regular exercise, the very best way to break down the unwelcome toxic body deposits and send them scurrying out of your body is to do regular body brushing.

Buy a natural, *not* a synthetic, bristle brush. Sisal is great. One with a long handle makes it easier to reach all areas of your body. Even better would be one that had a removable head with a strap for your hand, for easy reach to all areas.

Daily 3–5 minute body brush routine:

1 The best time to do it is first thing in the morning, prior to your bath or shower and on a dry, naked body.
2 Begin brushing your skin in long sweeping strokes starting from the soles of your feet. The nerve endings in the soles of your feet affect the whole body. Next brush the ankles, calves, and thighs, then brush across your stomach and buttocks and lastly brush your hands and arms upwards. Always brush towards the heart, but you can use circular movements over the tummy. Try and brush several times in each area, overlapping as you go. Maintaining the long sweeping strokes, concentrate on problem areas such as hips, thighs and upper arms with extra strokes. It shouldn't take longer than three minutes. Be careful to avoid sensitive areas and anywhere the skin is broken (skin rashes, wounds, cuts, infection or sunburn).

Top Tip: Don't be tempted to only brush your cellulite areas in an attempt to 'save time'. If you leave out the sweeping movements over the whole body, you don't actually boost the lymphatic flow, which is what is you need to do in order to remove the toxic build-up. Concentrating on the cellulite areas will only help to break them down a bit more if combined with the sweeping movements over the whole body.

---

3 Have a warm (not hot) shower. For an extra circulation booster, have a blast of cold water before you get out.
4 Gently dry off and massage some moisturizer into your skin.

> Top Tip: Don't forget that you are using your body brush to remove your own dead skin cells. These will build up in the brush, so it's a good idea to regularly clean your body brush using soap and water. I would say once a week is best. After rinsing, dry your skin brush in an open, preferably sunny spot to prevent mildew.

Body brushing is more effective on dry skin because when it is wet, the skin stretches and the effect isn't quite the same. Having said that though, doing it on wet skin would be better than not doing it at all! You can use the body brushing technique in the bath or shower using a loofah or mitt, or you can wash using a grainy scrub.

> Top Tip: You can make your own body scrub by mixing some water or olive oil into a paste with a handful of sea salt, dried oatmeal, uncooked rice, crushed sesame seeds, or wheat-germ.

Moisturizing

In order to keep the skin on our body supple and stop it from getting dry and scaly, it is important to moisturize every time that we bath or shower. While we are washing the dirt off our bodies we also remove the protective layer of sebum that holds all the moisture in our skin. Our skin then absorbs some of the water that it is in contact with, but without its 'barrier', as soon as we step out of the bath or shower, it has all evaporated, leaving the skin dry and crying out for some moisture. This whole process takes only three minutes. So if you can manage to slather your moisturizer on within three minutes of getting out of the shower, you will able to lock in all the water that your skin absorbed while you were wet.

> Top Tip: Alternatively, you can rub some body oil (nut or seed oils are good for this) onto the skin while you are still in the shower, ensuring that you lock all that extra moisture in. Make sure that you just pat yourself dry when you get out though – if you rub, you will just rub all the oil off. Also, be very careful that the floor of your bath or shower doesn't get slippery.

- *Eczema skin* If you have eczema on your body you might want to try having a bath with dead sea or hydro active mineral salts. The high concentration of minerals dissolves away any dead skin cells and helps the body to release toxins. Don't wash with soap, instead use an aqueous or emollient cream massaged well into the skin to lift off dirt while protecting the skin from drying out.
- *Hands* Our hands are constantly exposed to the weather and to water and are most often dry and dehydrated. Because of this, no matter how well we are applying all our best anti-ageing strategies to the skin on our face, our hands will often give the game away. The best thing that we can do for our hands is to try and moisturize them every time that we wash them, just like our bodies. Keeping a hand cream next to the soap is a good way to remember. SPF is also vital to help keep hands looking as young as possible.
- *Feet* Our feet work very hard to support us all day, but like hands, they are often neglected. A pedicure is a nice treat and can be a great way to take some time out for yourself. You don't even have to go to a salon for a professional one, you can also do it yourself at home:

DIY home pedicure:

- Soak feet for ten minutes in a bowl of warm water with a couple of drops of your favourite essential oil, or even a tiny bit of bubble bath.
- Dry them and clip your toenails and file any rough edges.
- Use an exfoliating scrub or a pumice stone to work on any areas of rough skin (usually the heels and the balls of the feet), then wash the feet off and dry them again.

Top Tip: To make a homemade strawberry foot scrub, mix 6–10 mashed strawberries with 2 tablespoons of olive oil and 3 tablespoons of sea salt.

- Apply a foot cream or body lotion using small circular motions, carefully working in between the toes and all over the foot.
- Apply a nail polish if desired, or give your toenails a quick buff for a natural shine.

Hair removal

Even though hair grows naturally on our legs, under our arms and around our bikini line, it is pretty much taken as a given that we will remove it. Women who don't meticulously groom themselves are either seen as feminist radicals who are making some kind of a statement, or they are seen as having 'let themselves go'. Therefore, we are all looking for the most suitable method for our own particular needs and our lifestyle. I am a fan of the rotary epilator myself – you get used to the pain and I feel a bit more in control than with waxing.

Methods of hair removal

Shaving

A razor is used to cut the hair off at skin level.

Good for: legs and armpits and some people also do their bikini line, but it can be easily irritated

Lasts for: 2–4 days

Pros: it is inexpensive, quick and easy

Cons: regrowth is fast and stubbly and if you are not careful you can cut yourself

Salon or home: home

Tips:

- Make sure that your blade is always sharp and go slowly.
- A shave oil gives the closet shave and is the kindest to the skin, especially if you are sensitive. Make sure to rinse your blade with hot running water though.
- Shave when you are just about to finish your bath or shower when the pores are more open and the hairs softer – you will get a closer shave and you are less likely to get a rash.
- Safety blades minimize the chances of nicks and cuts.

Waxing

Hot or cold wax is applied to the hairs and they are pulled out by the root.

Good for: all areas

Lasts for: 3–6 weeks

Pros: can last longer than other temporary types of hair removal; skin is left very smooth, regrowth is soft and downy

Cons: hair needs to be at least 5 mm long to do a good job. It can be painful and the skin can become temporarily irritated and uncomfortable. Not recommended if you have sensitive skin.

Salon or home: both

Tips:

- Avoid using deodorants or fragranced lotions for 12 hours, on any areas that have been waxed.
- Avoid the sun, sunbeds and hot showers for 12 hours.

Sugaring

Similar to waxing, but instead of wax, a sugar paste is used.

Good for: sensitive or thin skin such as armpits and bikini line

Lasts for: 4–6 weeks

Pros: can be less painful than waxing, as the paste sticks to the hair rather than the skin; soft downy regrowth

Cons: can be sticky and messy and hair needs to be a certain length

Salon or home: both

Epilating

Like an electric shaver, but instead of cutting the hairs off, small discs rotate and pull the hairs out by the root.

Good for: all areas, most machines now have special attachments for more delicate areas like underarms and bikini line

Lasts for: 4–6 weeks

Pros: easier and less messy than home waxing or sugaring and hair can be any length; soft downy regrowth

Cons: it can be painful

Salon or home: home

Tips:

- Avoid exfoliating directly before or afterwards as the skin can be too sensitive.
- Ice wrapped in a flannel can soothe any post-epilation redness.
- Best done after your bath or shower when the pores are open and the hairs are easier to remove.

Depilatory creams

These dissolve any hairs that they come into contact with at skin level.

Good for: legs, short fine hairs and smaller areas

Lasts for: 4–10 days

Pros: easy to do and doesn't hurt and regrowth can be smoother than shaving

Cons: thicker, stronger hairs sometimes need two goes; it can be quite messy and many people don't like the smell; not good if you have sensitive skin

Salon or home: home

Tips: read the instructions carefully and don't leave it on the skin for longer than the recommended time.

Electrolysis

A fine needle is inserted into the hair follicle and it sends an electric current through the hair, killing it at the root.

Good for: small areas such as the face or bikini line

Lasts for: after a course of treatments, it can be permanent

Pros: it can be permanent

Cons: it can be expensive, it takes quite a long time and it can be painful

Salon or home: should only be done by a qualified therapist.

Laser hair removal

A laser 'zaps' the hair root and kills it.

Good for: until recently, this was only recommended for people with light skin and dark hair, but recent developments in technology mean that it is possible for a wide variety of different coloured hair and skin types

Lasts for: 6 months to permanent

Pros: long-lasting hair removal and large areas of hair can be treated at once

Cons: it can last longer for different people; it can be expensive and uncomfortable

Salon or home: laser hair removal should only be done by a qualified technician

Tips: avoid sun exposure directly before or after treatment as this can cause discolouration that can last for months.

Dealing with ingrown hairs

An ingrown hair occurs when a hair fails to reach the follicle opening and curls back on itself sometimes becoming trapped under a fine layer of skin. At other times, sebum (oil) can build up around the hair and cause it to become infected and swollen and sometimes sore. Ingrown hairs can be an unfortunate by-product of hair removal, but regular exfoliation and moisturizing to keep the skin clear and soft can also go a long way to preventing the chance of ingrown hairs.

Gentle, daily exfoliation can often get rid of the 'non-angry' hairs that you can see under the surface. Be careful picking at the more angry ones – just like with spots, you could end up with a scar. The safest way to deal with them is to apply an ingrown hair lotion that will dry up the skin and draw the offending hair to the surface where it can be easily removed with a pair of sterilized tweezers. Like spot treatments, lotions including tea tree oil, or salicylic acid should do the trick.

Skin care *(the right kind for you)*

As a make-up artist, the thing that I get asked more than anything (apart from 'which celebrities have you worked with?'), is 'please can you make me look like I have beautiful skin?' While some clever concealing and some make-up magic can transform almost anyone, the best results come from skin that doesn't need much work in the first place, that is, skin that is good from the inside.

Good skin is more about how you conduct your life, rather than what you put on it. Beautiful skin = healthy skin, and as our skin reflects what is going on inside our bodies, our lifestyle is a major factor in the condition of our skin. All the elements of the ingredients for our beauty 'cake' have a direct effect our skin: sleep, water, diet, self-esteem, happiness, stress levels, posture, exercise, sun and free radical action. Therefore, good health and vitality lead to good skin, which enhances beauty.

The reverse of this is also true. We need to take care of our skin, because it takes care of our body. We must also allow for the part that the mind plays in this equation. When we are happy, we generally have good skin, when we are under stress, the first place it tends to show is our skin. This can also work in reverse. Poor skin can have a negative effect on self-esteem and when our self-perception changes, it changes the way we relate to other people, which in turn changes the way they relate to us, creating a negative atmosphere.

How does our skin work?

In the same way that it is much easier to understand how to take care of our bodies if we first understand a little bit about how they work, it is also much easier to understand how to take good care of our skin if we first understand how that works.

The skin is the body's largest organ. It has many functions. Apart from literally holding us together, it protects our insides against injury and attack from harmful bacteria, it insulates us and has an inbuilt thermostat and pre-programmed temperature control and it acts like a control centre for sending and receiving sensory information. We also get rid of toxic waste through our skin and, without realizing it, we even do a lot of our breathing through our skin! It is as much of an essential organ to the functioning of the body as any of the other vital organs (e.g. heart, liver, kidneys), and it is also the first area that will show signs of stress, which means that even if you are blessed with good genes and great skin, you still need to look after it as best you can.

Epidermis

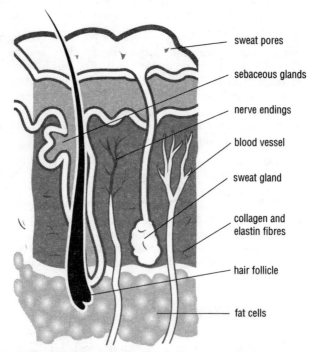

sweat pores

sebaceous glands

nerve endings

blood vessel

sweat gland

collagen and elastin fibres

hair follicle

fat cells

figure 2.1 diagram of the skin

Epidermis

The outermost layer of the skin, or *epidermis*, is made up of many tiny layers – think filo pastry but millions of times thinner (see Figure 2.2). It acts as a protective barrier and is responsible for keeping water inside the body and for keeping harmful bacteria out. The innermost layers are made up of juicy, living cells and the outermost layers are actually made up of dead cells.

The skin naturally sheds this outer layer like a conveyor belt system, and as it does so, new healthy, juicy cells take their place at the beginning of the chain. If left to its own devices, this process would take quite a while, and like water that is left in a hole for a long time, it can get stagnant. Running water, however, is always fresh and skin works the same way: if we encourage our skin to shed its dead outer layer as often as possible, we encourage fresh new cells onto the conveyor belt all the time, ensuring that our skin is always at its freshest and healthiest. The most effective way to encourage the skin to shed its dead outer layer is to regularly exfoliate. I'm not a big fan of harsh scrubs as these can often be abrasive and do more harm than good, but using a gentle exfoliant can often yield remarkable results. Not only does the texture of the skin

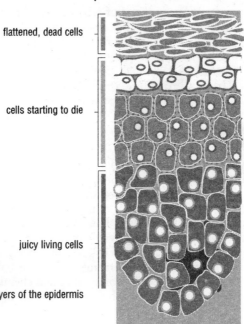

flattened, dead cells

cells starting to die

juicy living cells

figure 2.2 the layers of the epidermis

improve, but also so does its ability to absorb any moisturizers or cream that you might apply afterwards, so it's like a double bonus. There is more detailed information on exfoliation later in this chapter.

Dermis

Underneath this layer is the *dermis*. As well as housing the skin's blood and nerve supply, hair follicles and sweat glands, the dermis is also home to the sebaceous glands (see below). It is made up of a mesh-like structure of collagen and elastin fibres, which act as the support system for the skin (see below). All the new cells that move onto the conveyor belt in the epidermis are made here in the dermis. The cells in the dermis are the ones that actually absorb the moisture from the moisturizer that we put on our skin, and because they get 'plumped up' so the skin appears 'plumped up' and therefore more youthful. This is another reason not to let the outer layer 'stagnate' – it is much harder for moisturizer to penetrate the cells in the dermis if it first has to get through loads of build-up of old dry dead cells in the epidermis.

Sebaceous gland

The dermis contains millions of sebaceous glands which secrete *sebum*, an oily substance, that sits on top of the surface of the skin and acts as the skin's natural lubricant and waterproof protection barrier, preventing the skin from drying out. Generally sebum is deposited on the hairs inside the follicles (see Figure 2.1) and is brought up to the surface of the skin along the hair shaft. In hairless areas, the sebum surfaces through ducts. The level of sebum secretion is controlled by our hormones and can sometimes be very high due to extreme hormonal activity in response to things like puberty or stress.

This layer of sebum on top of our skin mixes with the sweat that our skin releases to form a protective barrier. This barrier is slightly acidic and has a pH level of between 4.5 and 5.5, and is sometimes called the acid mantle (see below for more information on pH levels). This 'acid mantle' acts like a waterproof barrier stopping water from evaporating from the skin, and also protecting the skin from being attacked by bacteria. It is important to remember that the balance of this acid mantle is easily upset by some soaps and chemicals and that in order to keep it doing its job properly, we need to be careful, firstly, not to strip it away, and then, secondly, to keep it balanced.

The chemical symbol for the measurement of acidity and alkalinity is pH (potential hydrogen in a water soluble solution). The entire external envelope of the human body, including skin, hair and nails is mildly acidic: pH 4.5–5.5.

pH	Type	Substance
0	Acid	Battery acid
1	Acid	Gastric juices, hydrochloric acid
2	Acid	Lemon/lime juice, cola
3	Acid	Vinegar
4	Acid	Wine, beer, tomatoes
5	Acid	Human skin
6	Acid	Milk
7	Neutral	Pure water
8	Alkaline	Sea water
9	Alkaline	Hand soap, baking soda
10	Alkaline	Milk of magnesia, cuticle softener
11	Alkaline	Ammonia, hair relaxer
12	Alkaline	Bleach
13	Alkaline	Oven cleaner
14	Alkaline	Liquid drain cleaner

Collagen

Collagen fibres start life as a tight supportive mesh and they get their tensile strength by holding onto water. As we get older this mesh loses some of its strength and at a certain point just isn't quite so springy any more – like a pair of knickers that have been through the wash a million times (see elastin, below). Because of its relationship with water, therefore, it follows that dehydrated skin develops wrinkles because there isn't enough water to keep the collagen moist. All the more reason to be drinking our two litres of water a day, but also to eat foods that have high water content and contain nutrients that repair and strengthen the cells. For more information on both these topics, please refer to the section on hydration (page 19) and nutrition (page 24).

Top Tip: Vitamin C plays an important role in the formation of collagen. Boost your daily intake by eating a Vitamin C-packed piece of fruit every day at breakfast.

Top Vitamin C fruits:
Kiwi fruit
Strawberries
Grapefruit
Orange

Elastin

Collagen fibres contain elastin, which (as the name suggests) acts like elastic. It is stretchy. When overstretched, however, elastin fibres rupture, resulting in stretch marks. Over time, oxidation causes the elastin fibres to lose their ability to hold onto water, therefore losing their elasticity. Oxidation in the skin is a result of many things and is usually a combination of: free radical action (see the section on free radicals in Chapter 1), general expressive use, incorrect skin care routine and a less than balanced lifestyle (see the section on balancing the ingredients in Chapter 1, page 4). Together with gravity, this loss of elasticity means that the skin inevitably begins to slacken, and because our eyes and mouth are our most expressive body parts, they end up suffering first.

Identifying your skin condition and skin stage

- The first step towards a glowing complexion is to learn how to identify the condition that your skin is in – this will help you to make sure that you are not doing more damage than good by using the wrong types of products.
- The second step is to identify your skin stage. Most people refer to this as your age, but in my experience, someone's chronological age doesn't always match with the 'age' of their skin.

Skin condition

By 'skin condition', I am referring mostly to the texture of the skin, or how it feels. For many years now we have been putting ourselves into 'skin type' boxes like: normal, oily, dry and combination. But I don't really believe that any one of us can fit into a particular 'skin type' box – and if we do then most of us are some form of 'combination', but not necessarily the same combination as the next person, which is why I prefer to say that we need to learn to identify our skin's condition – as this can change regularly depending on many factors.

Types of skin condition:

- normal or balanced – babies have this skin
- dry: dehydrated or dehydrated oil dry – dry skin is the most common skin condition
- oily – darker skins are more prone to oiliness (although not exclusively)
- sensitive – fairer skins are more prone to sensitivity (although not exclusively)
- acne – most prominent in puberty, but can also be a result of stress
- pigmented – most prominent in more mature skin
- eczema – an inflammatory skin disorder that is very common these days.

Things that can affect our skin's condition:

- hormones
- our age
- the level of nutrition in our diet
- how effectively the body digests its food
- the amount of sleep we get
- the amount of exercise we do
- the amount of water we drink
- the climate/weather
- living or working in central heating or air-conditioning
- illness
- stress levels
- free radical exposure
- the ingredients in our skin care and make-up.

Any one or combination of these factors can leave our skin dehydrated, too oily, not oily enough, sensitive, acne-prone, pigmented or visibly aged. It can also be different for different parts of your face at different times and in order to know what you need to do for it, you need to know how to identify each condition.

How to identify your skin condition

Correctly identifying your skin condition means having a good look at your skin as it is right now, not just going along with what you thought it was a few years ago, or what you think it should be. Get into the habit of looking at your skin every day, it doesn't have to take long, but the more of a habit you get into, the more aware of the subtle changes you will become and the better you will be able to adapt your skin-care routine to match. After a while it will all become second nature and your skin will be in the best condition that it can possibly be in.

> The tissue test: This is a great way to evaluate surface oil or sebum levels on the skin. Do this on clean, unmade-up skin, preferable not directly after waking up; give the skin some time to settle first.
>
> Take a piece of tissue and fold it over a couple of times to make a pad. Gently pat it on the area that you wish to test; any oil residue on the skin will be clearly visible on the tissue. Ideally you are looking for a tiny bit of residue all over the face, signalling a normal level of sebum on the surface. Most of us have slightly more oil across our foreheads and down the centre of our faces, the T-zone, so slightly more residue is to be expected here. No residue at all, or too much and skin will fall into one or more of the categories below. Remember that these skin conditions can fluctuate and do not necessarily apply to the whole face.

Getting into the habit of monitoring your skin is also good practice from a general health point of view, as you can keep an eye on any skin tags or moles. If they change shape, colour, get an uneven border, itch or bleed you are more likely to notice and consult your GP straight away, which will lessen any risk involved in the event that it is something serious.

Normal or balanced skin

Otherwise known as perfect skin. This is skin that is silky smooth to the touch, moist and plump looking. It is not too greasy and not too dry, it's not too thin and not too thick. It has no visible open pores, has a good colour and a healthy glow, with no wrinkles and fine lines. As you can imagine from the description, this is extremely rare and only really present in newborn babies who haven't yet had any exposure to any of the things that can start to change the texture and behaviour of our skin. This is basically the skin that we try to recreate using make-up.

Dry skin

Dry skin is the most common skin condition and it can be dehydrated or it can be dehydrated and oil dry.

Dehydrated skin

This is skin that has normal oil content but not enough water. Its appearance is usually a bit dull, dry and flaky. Lines can appear very easily around the eyes and mouth. Even though there isn't enough water in the skin, it isn't lacking in oil, and therefore doesn't need a heavy oil-based moisturizer, which will only end up overloading the skin and possibly leading to breakouts.

Do the tissue test to see if you have any oil or sebum residue on the driest parts of your face. If so, then you have dehydrated skin, and the best way to begin to rectify this is to increase your water intake. For more information about water, see the section on hydration in Chapter 1.

> Top Tip: All of the following things are dehydrating for the skin:
>
> hay fever and cold medication
> central heating and air conditioning
> saunas
> a diet of processed, sweet and fatty foods
> smoking or smoky environments
> coffee
> alcohol

Dehydrated and oil-dry skin

This is dehydrated skin that is also lacking in oil or sebum, meaning that it has no protective barrier. Therefore the skin is not able to retain any moisture that may be present. Dehydrated and oil-dry skin is visibly dry and flaky and it usually feels tight after washing. It doesn't have visible pores or follicles but is prone to wrinkles and chaps easily – most easily noticeable on the lips (as the lips have no protective sebum anyway.) This skin condition becomes more common as we get older and our natural sebum secretion slows down. In younger people it is most commonly the result of using inappropriate skin-care products. Using soaps, detergents or alcohol-based products or astringents will strip the skin's sebum barrier, leaving it unprotected and allowing any water to evaporate. The ingredients in skin-care products are explained in more detail later in the chapter.

Do the tissue test on the driest part of your face. If there is absolutely no residue or possibly even flakes of dry skin, then that area is dehydrated and oil dry and you will need to encourage the skin to normalize and retain its own moisture. This is when a rich oil-based moisturizer can be appropriate.

Oily skin

Oily skin has too much sebum on the surface. Most people tend towards being a bit oilier across their forehead and down the centre of their face, often referred to as the T-zone. This is because there are more sebaceous glands and larger follicles in those areas, as is the case on our back. Because of this, I tend to regard an oily T-zone more as a 'normal' condition. Oily skin appears shiny all over, has few wrinkles but visibly open pores. The greasy surface is a trap for dust and dirt and make-up, making it prone to clogging up and therefore more vulnerable to breakouts of spots and blackheads.

> *Spots and blackheads* form when a follicle becomes blocked up with a mixture of dead skin and sebum or oil. The only difference between a spot and a blackhead is that spots form under the surface and are closed. Blackheads are at the surface and open. Blackheads are black as a result of being exposed to the air and being oxidized. Spots become inflamed and pus-filled because that is the body's immune system's way of trying get rid the blockage.

Oily skin is pretty easy to identify, but if in doubt, the tissue test will confirm. Oily skin can be a great thing as it is less ageing because it is constantly being moisturized. When the oil is excessive, however, it does need to be carefully controlled, as it is very easy to use products that strip the oil away too much, resulting in the skin producing even more.

Oily skin can be either genetic, or a result of excess sebum production. Excess sebum is produced due to over-activity of the sebaceous glands triggered by hormonal activity. This is most apparent in puberty, during the monthly cycle and as a result of stress. As sebum production lessens with age, oily skin also tends to lessen with age.

Sensitive skin

This can be either constant, or something that we experience only sometimes. Sensitive skin can sometimes be hard to visibly see or it can appear red and or inflamed. It can feel sensitive to the touch and can be easily irritated by heat products and/or friction. Often there is a stinging sensation when certain products are applied. If you experience a reaction to something, you are not necessarily allergic; it could just mean that for whatever reason your body is more sensitive sometimes. If there are other things going on in your body or mind, the body might just not have enough resources to cope with something new, and instead of trying to deal with it, it just says 'no, not today' and rejects it.

Sensitive skin, apart from being genetic, can be caused by stress (mental or physical), friction, certain ingredients in skin-care products or make-up, medication, sun exposure and environmental pollution. It is also more prone to wrinkles and fine lines because it can be thin and often has a lack of oil.

Acne skin

Acne is an inflammatory skin disorder caused by over-production of sebum in the skin. Acne skin is oily with lots of spots and is often red and sensitive. There are different grades of acne – at the milder end you are dealing with a breakout, at the more severe end some of the spots can turn into cysts and removal can leave scarring.

Acne can be genetically inherited, it can be caused by cosmetics or it can be triggered by hormonal activity. When hormones called androgens are released into the body, they trigger sebum production, which can then result in oily skin and lead to acne symptoms. Androgens are the main hormones that are released when the body goes through puberty, which is why many of us are spotty during our teenage years. What many people don't realize, though, is that androgens are also released into the body as part of its stress response. So if you have ever been stressed in the past and then wondered why, as if to make matters worse, you also woke up with a breakout, the stress itself was most likely the cause. More information about stress and how to alleviate it are detailed in the section on stress, page 41.

Pigmented skin

Pigmentation on the skin appears as brown, black or white markings in patches that look like freckles. They appear over time on sun-exposed areas of the skin and are most common on the backs of the hand, face and legs, although they can also appear over the shoulders, back, chest and on any other areas that have had extensive sun exposure. They are superficial collections of skin pigment called melanin (the same pigment that protects us from sunburn by giving us a tan), which have accumulated within the top layer of skin (the epidermis). They usually appear later in life and can appear in conjunction with any skin condition. They can sometimes join together into patches that look like a dirty mark.

Although sun damage is the main cause of pigmentation in the skin, it can also occur as a result of pregnancy, stress hormones, fatigue and certain medications (especially oral contraceptives). Unlike pigmentation related to sun damage, pigmentation that occurs as a result of hormonal activity (e.g. pregnancy or oral contraceptives) generally disappears when balance is restored to the body.

Eczema/dermatitis

Eczema and dermatitis are interchangeable terms that describe an inflammation of the skin which may appear dry and flaky and will often feel hot and itchy. Sometimes, itchy blisters form which can burst leaving the surface moist and crusty. Eczema can affect just a small patch of skin anywhere on the face or body, or it can affect the whole body. Often, in the commonest form of eczema (atopic eczema), the problem is worst in the folds of the skin where your limbs bend. The itch is intense and makes you want to scratch. You should avoid this if you possibly can, as scratching only makes the symptoms worse.

Many things can cause eczema. The commonest is a general allergic over-sensitivity. This sort of eczema is known as atopic eczema, and it is linked with asthma and hayfever and can flare up as a reaction to certain foods and when you are under stress, feel anxious, angry or worried. Foods that are often linked with eczema are wheat, eggs, peanuts, milk, fish and soy. Eczema can also be triggered by substances which irritate the skin chemically, or substances to which the body has become allergic. Whatever the cause of your eczema, the skin becomes more sensitive, and may react to cosmetics, soaps, detergents, etc. Eczema skin should be treated as sensitive skin.

If you think that you have eczema, consult your GP for more advice.

Skin stages

In my experience someone's chronological age doesn't always match with the age of his or her skin. All of the factors that affect the condition of our skin, will also have an effect of the skin's 'age' – we already know that exposure to the sun and free radical action damage and therefore 'age' the skin. Thankfully this is an area over which we have some control. Unfortunately, however, we don't have any control over our genetic make-up, which governs the rate at which our cells age internally, which is reflected by our skin externally.

How our cells age: The cells in our bodies are constantly reproducing and we can see this most visibly in our skin in the way it is constantly shedding dead cells to make room for new living ones. Each cell in our body contains the 'code' or blueprint that makes each of us unique – our DNA. Until we reach adulthood, this code gets perfectly copied into each new cell that we make. Imagine it as if it went through a photocopier each time. As photocopiers get older, sometimes the copies start to fade a little, and the copies aren't quite as perfect as they were in the beginning. This is what happens in the body as we get older. The copies of the blueprint start to become less exact as tiny bits of information get lost, resulting in the ageing of our cells. This is most visible in our skin and hair, but also affects our muscles and body in general. There isn't anything that we can do to influence this aspect of the ageing process as this is purely determined by our genetic make-up.

For me there are three main skin stages: early stage, mid-stage and later stage. If you can recognize which stage your own skin is at, you will be able to use the most appropriate products and skin-care routine in order to get the best results and therefore maximize your beauty potential.

How to recognize your skin stage

Early stage

In early stage, our skin renews itself easily and efficiently: it is able to retain enough moisture to keep itself looking fresh, and the complexion is smooth and refined. It is in good condition, it feels firm and has an even colour and a natural luminosity. If you have early stage skin, even though it is in good condition, now is the time to start getting into the habit of taking care of it. The signs of ageing are pretty much impossible to reverse, but they are very easy to slow down – and sometimes even prevent – if action is taken early enough.

Top Tip: Early stage skin doesn't last for long if you are going out partying a lot. Excessive alcohol dehydrates the skin leaving it looking parched. Cigarettes contribute to crinkles around the eyes and mouth, and lack of sleep drains any radiance out of the skin.

Mid-stage

Mid-stage skin should still have some natural radiance, even skin tone and firmness, and if sunscreen has been used regularly, it should also have very few obvious lines. If not, this is when early signs of sun damage will start to show. As part of the unavoidable ageing process, the epidermis, or outer layer of the skin, will be starting to get a bit drier and thicker, therefore some roughness or uneven patches may start to become visible. At this stage, tiny spots of pigmentation might also start to show. It's under the surface, however, where things will be really starting to slow down. The cells that are responsible for repairing our skin will start to become less active. The skin will start to become less elastic.

Top Tip: Even if you have left it till now to think about looking after your skin, you can still do a lot to slow down the journey to the next stage. Start being serious about sun protection and increase your hydration both internally and externally while giving your body a nutritional boost with things like Vitamin C to help with collagen production and with fighting free radicals. For more information on these subjects, please see Chapter 1.

Later stage

No matter how well we have looked after ourselves, at some point we will start to notice the signs of ageing in our skin. Later stage skin is often dehydrated and oil dry, it appears loose and has wrinkles and pigmentation. It is no longer smooth to the touch and is often lacking in tone, colour and radiance. This is mostly due to what is happening under the skin's surface. The body is producing less sebum. Oestrogen levels decline and the cells find it harder to retain moisture, resulting in dehydration.

Collagen production is slowing down, the skin becomes less elastic, the pores enlarge and the skin's support structure collapses resulting in wrinkles. Also, reduced blood flow means the skin isn't able to nourish cells or discourage the build-up of waste toxins.

Top Tip: Even at this stage, it is never too late to start taking positive action to protect your skin from external ageing (i.e. free radical damage from sun and pollution, etc.) You may not be able to turn the clock back, but you can certainly stop if from getting any worse. Good skin care at this stage can help to boost hydration levels and reduce the appearance of some of the wrinkles and pigmentation. Try to get into the habit of using sunscreen and try sleeping on your back to cut down on lines that can be caused by repetitively pressing your face against the pillow.

For those of us not blessed with perfect skin, all we can do is our best to make the most of what we have and try to realize our own personal beauty potential. Even those who have the good genes still have to work to keep their skin good, and we could all do with treating our bodies a little better and having less stress and less environmental pollution drying out our skin or triggering breakouts.

Just like the idea of the beauty cake – it's all about finding the balance, taking control of what you can, and not beating yourself up over what isn't in your control.

Skin care: the basic routine

Looking after your skin properly is not just about having a skin-care regime, it is about having the right regime for your skin. Using the wrong kind of skin-care routine for your skin can sometimes make any problems that you have worse instead of better! In this section I will not be recommending any particular products or brands, instead I would like to give you the knowledge that you need to make the right choice for you, on your own. You certainly don't have to spend a fortune on skin care in order to get good results, especially if you are using it correctly. Apart from great packaging though, the more expensive creams often have a higher concentration of active ingredients (the ingredients that do more than just moisturize). It is also important to remember that you need to be a little bit patient with your products, because although moisturized skin can seem plumped up and instantly healthier after application, it can sometimes take up to two months to see the results of some active ingredients.

When caring for our skin, we need to respect that it is a living, breathing organ and, as mentioned above, its needs will change over time, under various conditions and in certain climates. We need to learn to adapt our skin-care regime appropriately, learning to work with these changes, rather than fight against them. It is also important to remember that basically everyone has some level of 'combination skin'. Instead of blindly using a product that says it is for 'combination skin', it is much more beneficial to start tuning in to how your skin condition can fluctuate from day to day and adapt your skin-care routine accordingly.

For example, if you have an oily T-zone and dry cheeks (this is very common – my own skin is like this), the best plan of action is to cleanse with a product that will aggravate neither condition and then use separate moisturizers on each area. At first you might think that it is extravagant to have two different moisturizers, but actually, because you are only using half the amount of each, they will last the same amount of time, and the result will be skin that is more balanced. This is not only better for the health of your skin, but also a much better base for applying make-up onto.

Having said that, the main point of this book is that it's all about finding the balance, and for some people, this will all seem too much like hard work. So, if in doubt, just use an oil-free moisturizer all over. If a product is not right for you, your skin will tell you, and so long as you are paying attention, you will see it and be able to rectify it.

Top Tip: Steer clear of extremes of temperature in your skin-care routine: avoid anything too hot or too cold. Both heat and cold can aggravate thread veins and broken capillaries. High heat not only triggers dehydration, but also stimulates oil production. Instead of steaming your face, try a gentle facial massage. This will not only deep cleanse the face, but it will also stimulate circulation and exfoliate. There is more information about facial massage later in this section (pages 98–105).

To get the best out of your skin, use this routine, twice a day (morning and night). Try to be consistent, because the skin responds well to stability. Even if you only do the minimum, do it every day.

- A: cleanse
- B: exfoliate
- C: tone
- D: moisturize.

> Top Tip: If you only take one thing away from this chapter, try really hard to never go to bed with your make-up on. Make-up + dirt and grime + natural oils from the skin + more natural oils from the skin = a recipe for breakouts. The skin tries to repair itself while we sleep, but it can't do this properly if it is all blocked up with dirt, debris and make-up. When I come home late from a party and roll into bed, I have a packet of alcohol-free cleansing wipes in my bedside cabinet, and I can reach over and wipe my face clean without even having to open my eyes.

A: Cleansing

Cleansing is not just about removing make-up. At the end of the day, an unmade-up face will have an invisible layer of oil and sweat that has grabbed onto particles of pollution, dust, dirt and grime, and it is just as important to remove this as it is to clean off the day's make-up. Cleansing is a very important part of your skin-care routine because it ensures that the next two steps (exfoliation and moisturizing) work more efficiently.

How to cleanse:

- The skin needs to be cleansed twice daily: in the morning to clean off the dirt and dead skin cells that have attached themselves to the skin's acid mantle over night, and in the evening to clean off the day (as mentioned above).
- Apply either a water-soluble cream cleanser to dry skin, or a soap-free foaming or bar cleanser to damp skin. I prefer water-soluble or soap-free foaming cleansers, because rinsing off is gentler on the skin than wiping off.

> Top Tip: If using a cream cleanser, warm it slightly in the palms of your hands by rubbing them together, before applying it – this helps to emulsify the cream, therefore making it more effective.

- Massage the cleanser all over face and neck, working from the centre outwards. Don't rub too hard, as this can damage the skin's protective shield. Be gentle and thorough.

> Top Tip: Don't forget your neck when cleansing – the skin is quite fine here and shows age and damage much quicker than the face.

- Rinse with plenty of warm water (ten splashes usually does the trick) and check that you don't have any residue around the hairline, by the ears and in the creases if your nose. It is really important to rinse properly otherwise you are just left with an emulsion of dirt mixed in with a nice layer of soapy food for bacteria to feed on. Not rinsing properly can be just as bad for the skin as not cleansing in the first place.

> Top Tip: Rinse with warm water because rinsing with water that is too hot can damage the blood vessels under the skin, and cold water won't emulsify soap or dissolve dirt and oil.

Why use a 'soap-free' foaming cleanser, why not just use soap?

One of the most important things to remember while cleansing is that in order for your moisturizer to function properly, you need to clean the skin without stripping or unbalancing its natural protective barrier or acid mantle (see above). Soap, or any foaming cleanser that contains soap, strips this barrier and dehydrates the skin leaving it feeling dry, tight, itchy and uncomfortable. On top of that, a bar of soap that sits in your shower will hold onto any bacteria that you might have washed off your body the day before, and that warm, moist environment is the perfect breeding ground for them to multiply and be transferred back onto your skin the next day. Pretty yucky when you think of it like that! On top of that, I don't know anyone who would wash his or her hair with a bar of soap, so why would we wash our face with it? Also, the emulsifying agents in solid bars of soap are naturally alkaline and upset the skin's natural pH balance. For more information about pH balance, please see page 59.

Alternative cleansing

Using the balls of the fingers, gently massage almond oil or an unrefined vegetable oil (something like cold-pressed olive oil) all over your neck and face. Instead of an oil you could also use an aqueous cream. After massaging in, let this sit on the face for about a minute. Magically, the oil will dissolve all the grime and build-up, without stripping the face of its protective film. Remove by gently sweeping a dampened cotton wool pad over the whole area. This method of cleansing could be combined with the facial massage routine detailed later in this chapter pages 98–105.

Removing eye make-up

We need to be a little bit more careful when cleansing our eyes. Too much rubbing and scrubbing can stretch and damage the delicate skin. This is the best way to do it:

- Soak a cotton wool pad in warm water, squeeze out the excess, and then drop on a little eye make-up remover.
- Place the cotton wool pad over one eyelid and gently massage the eye area in a circular motion, through the pad using your fingertips.
- Repeat the whole process on the other eye with a new pad, and then cleanse your face.

B: Exfoliating

Exfoliation is about getting rid of the build-up of dead skin cells on the surface of the skin. Left to its own devices, the skin will shed these dead skin cells of its own accord, but because they cling onto the oil on the skin's surface, it will shed them in uneven clumps and the stagnant skin underneath may end up appearing dull and grey. Exfoliation refines the skin's texture and results in softer skin with fewer fine lines. Your skin will seem to be brighter and this radiance is caused by the boost in circulation. Getting rid of the unwanted layers not only helps the skin to do its job better (protecting the body and getting rid of toxins), but it also stimulates cell reproduction deep in the dermis, making us look and feel better. Exfoliation is good for every skin condition and skin stage and can even help with dark circles and puffy eyes. Exfoliation on the face should be done gently and regularly, I would say twice a week is good, but you can exfoliate more frequently when the weather is warm and humid. Some products are gentle enough that they can be used every day.

How to exfoliate:

- Choose an exfoliant that isn't too gritty as these can be harsh on the skin. Look for a gentle product – products containing sugar, salt, oatmeal or tiny synthetic grains or beads can be quite gentle. Avoid using scrubs if you use a Retin-A product, or if you've got broken capillaries, rosacea, acne or eczema.

Top Tip: You can make your own scrub at home by mixing a couple of teaspoons of oatmeal or wheat bran with a teaspoon of almond or cold-pressed olive oil.

- After cleansing, dampen your face and neck.
- Apply exfoliant using your fingertips (not a washcloth) to gently roll the scrub over your skin, using stroking rather than scouring motions in an upward direction and with a light touch.
- Don't forget under the eyes, behind the ears and on top of the eyelids (but be careful not to get any product in your eye – if you do rinse out with cool water).
- Take as long as you have time for, up to two minutes.
- Then rinse well with warm water (ten splashes usually does the trick) and check that you don't have any residue around the hairline, by the ears and in the creases if your nose.
- Pat dry with a towel, try not to rub, as rubbing with the towel works to exfoliate as well (see below) and this could be too harsh for the skin.

Top Tip: If your face stings a bit when you apply your moisturizer afterwards, then you've been a bit too harsh. Let your skin settle and wait at least a week before trying again, and be a bit gentler the next time.

Alternative exfoliating:

- *The time-saving version*: If that all seems like a bit of a palaver, try rubbing your face gently with a towel (sideways is better than up and down). You can do this easily after cleansing and it will hardly add any time to your normal skin-care routine. It doesn't work quite as deeply as using a grainy exfoliator or an AHA product (see below), but can still be an effective way to remove dead skin cells.
- *The pampering version*: This one is great to do while relaxing in a nice bath. Apply a clay-based mask, or any mask that hardens as it dries. This not only deep-cleans the skin, but also acts as a great once-a-week exfoliator; all the dead skin cells and excess surface oil are washed away when you rinse the mask off. If you are going to try this, don't combine it with a daily scrub or AHA product (see below), as this will be too harsh on the skin.

- *The chemical version*: Dead skin cells can also be loosened chemically using products that contain fruit acids called alpha hydroxy acids, or AHAs. AHAs dissolve the bonds that hold dead cells on the skin. Look for products containing glycolic acid, citric acid, malic acid or lactic acid. It is quite possible that AHAs can sting when you first start using them, but stop using any product immediately if your skin goes red or feels like it's burning. Consult your GP if you are at all concerned. Where AHA products are concerned, I would stick with one brand and make sure to follow the instructions carefully.

It is also possible to exfoliate the skin using DIY microdermabrasion kits and peels, although I wouldn't advise trying anything like this without speaking to a skin specialist first. They can help with the removal of dead skin cells, but using them incorrectly or too much can result in the skin becoming permanently sensitized and make it more vulnerable to damage from sunlight and the environment.

C: Toning

In the past, toners were mostly used to remove any remaining traces of make-up, oily cleanser, or soap film left after cleansing. If we are cleansing properly with water soluble, soap free cleansers, this is no longer necessary. But we can use toners to close the pores and tighten the skin, boosting circulation and helping to protect the skin while also helping to restore its pH balance after cleansing and exfoliating.

How to tone:

- Look for a toner or freshener that has an astringent effect but that doesn't contain alcohol. Alcohol dehydrates the skin, which can block impurities beneath the surface. It can also damage the collagen below the surface. Watch out for witch hazel, as it can also dry the skin, although would work fine if balanced with vitamin E or honey.
- After cleansing (and exfoliating), apply a small amount of toner to a damp cotton wool pad and sweep lightly over the whole face.
- While your face is still damp, apply your moisturizer. This locks in all the moisture.

Top Tip: For a more refreshing tone, spritz your toner onto your face. If it doesn't come in a spray bottle, you can transfer it yourself.

Alternative toning:

You can make you own toner at home using soothing herbal tea. Camomile, marigold, rosehip or nettle teas work the best. Because of the essential oils, don't use this recipe if you are pregnant without first checking with your GP.

Home-made herbal tea toner recipe:

• infuse a tea bag from the list above in a cup of boiling water
• add two drops of either orange or lavender essential oil
• leave to cool and your toner is ready to use
• you can transfer to a bottle and keep in the fridge for about a week.

Failing that, just splashing or spritzing the face with cool water before you apply your moisturizer will close the pores and give you a bit of moisture to lock in – you won't get the pH balance, but it would be better than nothing.

D: Moisturizing

Moisturizing is very important. Well-moisturized skin feels comfortable, soft and supple, it has a healthy glow and ages less quickly. When our bodies are lacking in water, it shows in our skin. The basic function of a moisturizer is to mimic the function of the skin's natural acid mantle. We want to lock moisture in, and hold it there with a waterproof barrier that has the appropriate pH balance to protect the skin from attack from bacteria.

How to moisturize

• Use the guide below to find a moisturizer that is right for your skin condition and stage. Expensive creams are not necessarily better for your skin, especially if they are the wrong kind for your skin condition or stage. The best plan is to use the lightest moisturizer possible for your skin type. Remember that moisturizers are not meant to be providing all your skin's moisture, they are meant to be helping your skin to better moisturize itself.

• Apply your moisturizer to slightly damp skin, directly after toning or splashing with cool water. Applying moisturizer this way, not only locks more moisture into the skin, but you will find that you don't need to use quite so much of it, so you are getting more for your money as well. A pea-sized blob should be plenty. Don't be tempted to apply too much. Overloading the skin with moisturizer can do just as much harm as not having enough.

- Gently massage the moisturizer into your skin using upward circular strokes, making sure not to pull or stretch the skin.

> Top Tip: Don't forget to moisturize down your neck – it doesn't have any sebaceous glands and makes no natural oil of its own. Because of this, it is extremely vulnerable to the effects of ageing, and is often the real 'giveaway' on someone who has had cosmetic surgery on their face to look younger.

In order to protect the skin from the damaging effects of the sun, we really need to be wearing sunscreen every day if we go outside (even if it is just walking to the station to go to work). If your moisturizer doesn't already contain sunscreen, it is best to wait about 15 minutes before applying it so as not to dilute its protection.

Ingredients

Ideally your moisturizer will contain some protection from the sun, in the form of SPF, and also some protection from free radical action in the form of antioxidant vitamins or minerals. For more information on SPF, free radicals and antioxidants, please see Chapter 1. Avoid anything containing too many petrochemicals like mineral oil, as they can dry the skin, block pores and prevent it from breathing and getting rid of waste. Products containing mineral oil are more likely to make our skin worse, not better. Aloe Vera, on the other hand, is great for skin care. Fresh aloe vera has been used for hundreds of years to effectively treat everything from dry skin, burns and insect bites to skin irritations, acne, cuts and abrasions. For more information on ingredients, please refer to the ingredients decoder (page 105).

> Top Tip: If you are worried that skin-care products may make you break out, look for ingredients that are 'non-comedogenic'. A comedone is the medical term for a spot or a blocked pore, therefore an ingredient that is non-comedogenic, is one that is highly unlikely to block pores and cause spots.

Night treatments

Night treatments can be great, especially for rectifying extreme skin conditions like dehydration that could have been caused by any number of reasons, for example: central heating, air conditioning, flying, illness, certain medications. They usually contain more active ingredients than day treatments and the reason that they work better is because the skin absorbs active ingredients better while we are asleep. There are more details about active ingredients in the ingredients decoder (page 105).

Alternative moisturizing

A small amount of cold-pressed olive oil gently massaged into the skin can be a simple yet effective alternative to a heavy night cream. This is not suitable for use in the daytime as the face stays quite shiny for a while after application. This is also definitely not suitable prior to applying make-up.

Adapting skin care to suit skin condition

Normal or balanced skin

This is basically perfect skin and is usually only present in new-born babies. If you have been very lucky with your genes and you have this beautiful, smooth, plump and even skin, it is very easy to care for and the best thing that you can do is not take it for granted.

- *Cleanser* Use any type so long as it is water-soluble and soap free.
- *Exfoliator* Nothing too harsh, and don't use too much on the T-zone as this may stimulate oil production.
- *Toner* Use any type, so long as it doesn't contain alcohol.
- *Moisturizer* Nothing too rich, preferably with SPF 15 for the daytime
- *Special care* For a treat now and then, try a nourishing mask (for tips on applying face masks, see the section on professional tips and tricks, page 187).

Dry skin

If you have dry skin, boost the work that your skin care is doing by helping from the inside too. To keep the skin hydrated, drink at least two litres of water a day and eat plenty of fluid-rich fruit and vegetables, such as: melon, grapefruit, strawberries, broccoli, cabbage, cauliflower, celery, aubergine, lettuce, bell peppers, radish, spinach, courgettes and tomatoes.

> Top Tip: Essential fatty acids, omega 3 and 6, are important to help keep skin soft and stop it from dehydrating. Good sources include tuna, salmon, halibut and sardines; nuts and seeds; vegetable oils.

- *Cleanser* Try to find a water-soluble cleanser that is creamy and moisturizing. Avoid the foaming ones as they tend to be a bit more drying. Almond milk, coconut milk and apricot oil can be individually used as natural cleansers. If your skin is dehydrated and oil dry, a great alternative is to cleanse using a cleansing balm as these have high oil content.

- *Exfoliator* Creamy, gentle AHAs work best, but avoid these if your skin is at all sensitive. The home-made scrub (page 74) would work well on dry skin.

- *Toner* Use a rose water toner or something gentle. You could try one of the herbal tea infusions (page 76), using two drops of either rose or sandalwood essential oil in place of the orange or lavender, but not if you are pregnant without first checking with your GP.

- *Moisturizer – dehydrated* Look for skin-care products that contain humectants and preferably SPF 15. Humectants are substances that attract water to the skin to hold in moisture. Sorbitol (made from glucose), vegetable glycerine, vitamin B5 and vitamin E are all natural humectants. Don't use a heavy night cream, but something light will encourage the skin to work for itself.

- *Moisturizer – dehydrated and oil dry* Look for a richer, oil-based moisturizer containing preferably SPF 15. A facial oil at night time would provide extra nourishment.

Top Tip: Moisturizing ingredients to look for are cucumber, evening primrose oil, lavender and camomile.

- *Special care* A soothing hydrating mask is great for a treat, avoid clay masks though as they can be drying. For tips on applying face masks, refer to the section on professional tips and tricks (page 187).

Top Tip: Applying a hydrating serum can be a fantastic way to boost the skin's moisture levels and can work under or over moisturizer depending on the product. I use them a lot at work because so many people have just been on long flights and their skin is parched and needs a quick fix before the make-up application. If I use one together with a facial massage, the client feels like they have a new face! For more details on facial massage see pages 98–105.

Oily skin

An oily barrier on the skin isn't such a bad thing to have because the skin is well protected and stays looking younger for longer. It can, however, be a bit of a magnet for dust and dirt and when the oil is excessive it does need to be brought under control. This is easily done with an appropriate skin-care plan.

Most people tend to be a bit oilier across their foreheads and down the centre of their faces, otherwise known as the T-zone. This is because the skin has more sebaceous glands there and if treated the same way as the rest of the face, it will generally balance out fine. I wouldn't necessarily treat the T-zone as 'oily' unless the oil production was excessive – for example, when hormones are raging during the monthly cycle, or if stress is triggering extra sebum production.

> Top Tip: Balance is the key with this skin condition. The larger pores mean that it is really important to keep oily skin clean but over-washing and harsh toning can strip the oil layer completely which sends a signal to the brain telling it to make even more oil to compensate. This can just end up making the problem worse in the long term.

- *Cleanser* Look for a water-soluble purifying cleanser or use a soap-free foaming gel or bar cleanser. Alternatively you could try mixing milk, honey and a few drops of lime as a home-made cleanser suitable for oily skin.
- *Exfoliator* Look for a gentle grainy scrub and use a gentle circling motion to concentrate on blackhead prone areas like nose and chin. Alternatively, something containing AHAs will help to smooth the skin's texture. As mentioned above though, beware of over-stripping the skin.
- *Toner* Use an alcohol-free purifying toner. Witch hazel is often recommended for oily skin, but make sure it is balanced with either vitamin E or honey to stop it from being too drying. You could also try one of the herbal tea infusions (page 76), using two drops of either juniper or lemongrass essential oil in place of the orange or lavender (if you are pregnant check first with your GP).
- *Moisturizer* It isn't true that oily skins don't need moisturizer – they just need a different kind from most other skin conditions. Anything too heavy will end up blocking the pores and causing problems, which is why something lightweight and oil free or even oil absorbing is more

appropriate, preferably containing SPF 15. Oil-absorbing or mattifying products dry on the skin's surface, minimizing the appearance of large pores and absorbing any excess oil, leaving you shine-free and making a perfect base for make-up. Good ingredients to look for are: calendula, chestnut, aloe vera and burdock.

> Top Tip: Apply your moisturizer very lightly. If you massage oily skin too much, it will stimulate the oil glands to produce more sebum and you will be back where you started.

- *Special care* Use a purifying deep-cleansing clay mask once a week to absorb excess oil and keep skin clean. If you haven't got one of these, chilled natural yoghurt applied as a face mask will draw out impurities from the skin. For the best way to apply your face mask, please refer to the professional tips and tricks (page 187).

Sensitive skin

When skin is sensitive, whether it is all the time, or just sometimes, it is important to be very careful so as not to aggravate it. Sensitive skin is often dry because it can lack oil and is therefore more prone to wrinkles and fine lines. It is therefore just as important to limit time in the sun, in air conditioning, in central heating and in other situations that would dry the skin out, as it is to use the correct kinds of products. As with dry skin, diet and water intake can also make a big difference. If you are worried, then stick with products that say they are 'hypoallergenic'. Also, I would advise avoiding anything that contains alcohol, soap, fragrance or lanolin. The ingredients decoder (page 105) contains more details about possible problem ingredients in skin care.

> Top Tip: The most important thing is to be gentle with your skin. Most skin-care experts agree that many of us are too rough on our skin in general. This is even more relevant if your skin is sensitive. Not only does this not get the best out of your skin, it certainly won't 'toughen it up', it will most likely just end up leaving it worse than how it started.

- *Cleanser* Look for an ultra-mild, unfragranced, water-soluble cream or lotion cleanser to minimize risk of irritation. Most soap-free foaming or bar cleansers will be too harsh for sensitive skin.

- *Exfoliator* Avoid scrubs and AHAs as they may also be too harsh.

> Top Tip: I would recommend using regular facial massage to exfoliate the skin. The stimulation of the skin's surface encourages and speeds up its natural shedding process. The double bonus is that it also stimulates the sebaceous glands to produce more oil, which can balance the fact that sensitive skin is often lacking in oil. There is a detailed facial massage routine at the end of this section.

- *Toner* As mentioned above, I would stay away from anything that contains alcohol or fragrance, but a soothing mist of rose water won't do any harm.
- *Moisturizer* Look for a comforting, oil-based moisturizer containing ingredients like camomile, aloe vera and vitamin E to soothe the skin while at the same time helping to create a protective barrier layer. Only use sunscreen products containing physical filters (e.g. titanium dioxide) as opposed to chemical sunscreens that may sink into the skin and cause irritation. Sunscreens are explained in greater detail in the section on the sun, page 13.
- *Special care* Have a special calming cream on hand for extra irritable days.

Acne skin

We can all suffer from spots or acne in varying degrees, and most of us will go to great lengths to try to get rid of our spots. Sometimes we don't even realize that our skin-care routine can actually be making our problem skin worse. This can either be because we are using inappropriate products, or because the ingredients in our products are actually doing more harm than good. Products that are not likely to cause acne are labelled as 'non-comedogenic'. For more information on ingredients that could be *comedogenic*, please refer to the ingredients decoder (page 105).

It is especially important with acne skin, not only to use the right products, but also to use them in the right way. It is very easy to want to strip the oil, scrub the spots and be far too harsh with acne-prone skin. But, as mentioned in the section on oily skin, stripping the skin will only make it produce more oil, and harsh scrubbing risks not only dehydration (and then more oil production) but also the spread of bacteria which can lead to more spots!

Top Tip: However tempting it might be, try not to squeeze or pick at your spots. Not only can this actually make acne worse by spreading bacteria, but you can also end up with scarring. A red, pus-filled spot is the body's way of dealing with an infection from bacteria that has lodged under the surface of the skin (usually from a blocked pore or hair follicle). The pus is full of white blood cells that are trying to heal the infection by destroying the bacteria. They destroy it by eating all the unwanted cells (a bit like Pac Man). Once they have done their job, the inflammation will go down and the spot will disappear. Most of us can't wait that long and we break the skin to squeeze the spot out, meaning that sometimes the white blood cells also eat some of the healthy skin tissue by accident, resulting in scarring. A better solution is to apply a treatment lotion that speeds up the process by exfoliating the surface cells, therefore encouraging the body to 'heal' the spot faster, and if you can't bear looking at it while it is healing, then follow the guide to clever concealing in the section on make-up (page 124).

- *Cleanser* Use a gentle soap-free foaming or bar cleanser to remove any impurities.
- *Exfoliator* Regular exfoliation is important if you have acne skin, because an excess of dead skin cells on the surface can contribute to acne. This can be done daily as long as it is gentle – remember, being too harsh can end up making the acne worse. Products containing *salicylic acid* or *benzoyl peroxide* work well to help exfoliate acne-prone skin.

Top Tip: A more natural alternative to benzoyl peroxide is tea tree oil, which has been clinically proven to be as effective, and is also much less irritating to the skin.

If your acne skin is also sensitive to product, exfoliate while cleansing the skin by gently rubbing it with a flannel or wash-cloth. Be sure to rinse it out well afterwards, or better still use a clean one each day.

- *Toner* Use an alcohol-free purifying toner. Witch hazel is often recommended for oily skin, but make sure it is balanced with either vitamin E or honey to stop it from being too drying. You could also try one of the herbal tea infusions (page 76), using two drops of either juniper or lemongrass essential oil in place of the orange or lavender, but not if you are pregnant without first checking with your GP.

- *Moisturizer* Look for something oil free that contains SPF 15. This is very important, because sunlight can cause damage and irritation to the skin, and once the skin is damaged, it increases the likelihood of an acne breakout.
- *Special care* If your acne is very severe, consult with your GP or dermatologist and you may be prescribed tablets or antibiotic lotions. It is important to remember, however, that many of the medications used to treat acne can dehydrate the skin and also make it more likely to burn if exposed to the sun. It is also important to give acne products enough time to do their job, and to use medications as directed. Using more medication than directed will not improve results. In fact, it can make acne worse by aggravating the skin. Be sure to read all labels and use accordingly or as instructed by your GP or dermatologist.

Eczema skin

Because eczema is essentially a sensitivity of the skin that can appear in varying degrees, like sensitive skin it is a condition that can either be permanent or can flare up as a response to certain situations (e.g. stress, allergies or illness). Many people are becoming more and more sensitive to our environment, whether it is to laundry detergents or household cleaners, or certain foods, and while avoiding exposure to things that may trigger reaction is recommended, this isn't always possible. It is now believed that increased intake of fish oils and evening primrose oil, as well as supplements of aloe vera can help to curb certain sensitivities, and by following a sensible skin-care routine, it is definitely possible to help to minimize your symptoms. However, if you have, or think that you have eczema, it is always best to follow the advice of your GP.

Top Tip: Try to avoid scratching when you itch, as scratching only serves to make the eczema worse. If you really can't stop yourself, then try gently stroking, with the flat of your hand, as this will provide a little relief without causing too much damage.

Antihistamine tablets be helpful in reducing the itch: check with your doctor.

- *Cleanser* Washing the skin tends to dry it out and can make eczema worse. With eczema skin it is very important to keep the skin supple and prevent it from drying out.

> Top Tip: Try using an aqueous or emollient cream as a substitute for soap. Massage the cream into the skin – you could try using the movements from the facial massage routine later in this chapter (pages 98–105). The oil from the cream will emulsify with the dirt and lift it away from the surface ready to be rinsed away. The great thing about an emollient cream is that you can also apply it directly to the skin any time it feels a bit dry or parched. Your GP, dermatologist or pharmacist will be able to recommend a good one.

Some special creams and oils that are good for eczema also contain an antiseptic because it has been found that eczema often flares up as a result of a germ infecting the skin, and antiseptics can stop this from happening.

- *Exfoliator* If you are cleansing your face using the facial massage routine, this will be stimulating the skin enough to encourage its own natural shedding process.
- *Toner* If your eczema is really angry, I would just splash or spritz with some cool water. Otherwise, a soothing mist of rose water shouldn't do any harm. Definitely avoid anything that contains alcohol or artificial fragrance.
- *Moisturizer* Moisturizing the skin is the mainstay of treating eczema and the best results come from creams and ointments that help to replenish the skin's natural protective oils. Your GP, dermatologist or pharmacist will be able to recommend the best one for you. Your GP may also prescribe a cream or ointment containing a steroid. These can be very effective at reducing inflammation and itch, but they should be used sparingly, and only while the eczema is bad as they can cause the skin to become thinner. They come in different strengths and are usually prescribed as the lowest strength that the skin requires at the time, in order to minimize the risk of possible side-effects. It is important to try to look at what is causing your eczema, though, as using steroid creams effectively pushes the problem back into the body only to return again at a later date.
- *Special care* The best thing that you can do to help with symptoms of eczema is to rest and relax, but a moisturizing mask now and then may help to alleviate dryness. For advice on how best to apply face masks, please see the professional tips and tricks in this chapter (page 187).

Ingredients that can aggravate eczema

Alcohol
Butadiene/acrylonitrile copolymer
Diammonium dithiodiglycolate
Glycol
Methyldibromo glutaronitrile
Potassium tallowate
Sodium lauryl sulphate
Sodium tallowate
Styren/acrylates/acrylonitrile copolymer

Pigmented skin

If you have pigmented skin, avoiding sun exposure is the best way to keep it under control.

> Top Tip: It is a good idea to avoid using self-tanners that stimulate the skin's own melanin production as this will only highlight the pigmented areas.

In order to minimize the appearance of pigmented skin, the safest approach is to use products that contain botanical (plant derived) skin brighteners. Ingredients to look for include liquorice, bearberry, rice, kiwi and mulberry, coupled with lactic acid and vitamin C. I would, however, advise checking with your GP, dermatologist or professional skin-care therapist before starting any skin-brightening treatment.

- *Cleanser* Choose the appropriate cleanser for the condition that the rest of your skin is in.
- *Exfoliator* Use a gentle scrub, or something containing AHAs, but not if you have darker skin that is also sometimes sensitive, as they can sometimes be problematic. Mandelic acid is a good alternative and is also good for oily and acne-prone skin.
- *Toner* Choose an appropriate toner for the condition that the rest of your skin is in.
- *Moisturizer* Look for a moisturizer containing antioxidant vitamins A, C and E and sunscreen of at least SPF 15.
- *Special care* A nourishing mask containing vitamins A, C and E will boost antioxidant activity and help to prevent the condition worsening. For advice on how best to apply face masks, please see the professional tips and tricks.

Adapting skin care to suit skin stage

Having determined your skin condition, which can fluctuate daily. The last variable in customizing your perfect skin-care routine depends on the stage that your skin is at. This will progress over time, and will be different for everyone. If you are already in the habit of paying attention to how your skin is behaving, you will very easily notice when you move from one stage to another. Putting it all together will result in your skin being able to function optimally and to look and feel its best. This will all feed into the 'cake' mix and together with all the other ingredients you will be well on your way reaching the goal of fulfilling your ultimate beauty potential.

For every skin stage, you should be assessing your skin condition regularly and using the appropriate products. Use these tips as extra advice to make everything work even better.

Early stage skin

It may seem like a drag, but starting to get into a routine of taking good care of your skin at this stage will guarantee that it stays looking younger for longer. Wrinkles are very difficult to get rid of, but they are simple to prevent. Lifestyle choices and skin-care routines put in place at this stage can literally change the life of your skin.

- Try to get into exfoliating twice a week, because together with keeping skin healthy and hydrated, it is one of the best ways to keep the skin at this stage.
- Whatever your skin condition, early stage skin should only need light moisturizing, but now is the time to get into the habit of applying daily a sunscreen of SPF 15.
- If your skin is dry, a great way to help prevent the onset of ageing is to use a serum together with your moisturizer in the winter months, when harsh weather conditions can start to damage otherwise healthy skin. Serums are light in texture and will boost the skin's water-retaining capacity without weighing it down or clogging it up.
- Try not to smoke or spend long amounts of time in the sun – nothing will age you faster.

Mid-stage skin

If you are already at mid-stage and you haven't really thought seriously about it before, then now is the time to start. Mid-stage skin still has some natural radiance, skin tone and firmness, but it will be starting to show visible signs of ageing in the form of fine lines and possibly mild pigmentation. Ultimately the goal of mid-stage skin care is to use moisturizing products to add water to the skin and seal in its own moisture. This doesn't erase wrinkles, but what it does do is plump up the skin cells for up to 12 hours (which is why you should moisturize twice a day.) There is no permanent change, but regular moisturizing makes your skin look better by making it look plumper, therefore making any lines or wrinkles less visible.

- Mid-stage skin can be starting to look a bit dull and feel a bit rough. This is because the cell renewal processes under the skin are starting to slow down. Regular exfoliation stimulates nerve endings, lymphatic circulation and blood flow. It also encourages the removal of dead skin cells, which in turn stimulates cell turnover. All of these things result in healthier, younger looking skin.

- Stimulate the circulation, and therefore the health and appearance of mid-stage skin by regularly massaging the face. Try the facial massage routine detailed later in this chapter (pages 98–105).

- Look for moisturizers that contain hyaluronic acid, which draws in water, or antioxidants like Vitamin E, Vitamin C, green tea or kinetin, to fight the effects of free radical damage and therefore help to combat the visible signs of ageing.

- For an extra shot of moisture, especially if your skin is dry, use a hydrating serum daily, in conjunction with your moisturizer. Serums are light in texture and help to calm and tone the skin. They are great for prevention as well as repair.

- Use an anti-aging serum, ointment or cream at night, giving all the active ingredients the best possible chance to work. Details about active ingredients and what they do are listed in the ingredients decoder (page 105).

- Boost your intake of vitamin C and protein. Vitamin C is not only a powerful antioxidant, the body also needs it in order to be able to make collagen. Eating protein is an important anti-ageing strategy because protein helps the body to repair and strengthen cell structure and it also stimulates collagen and elastin production to help keep the skin supple.

- Try not to smoke or spend long amounts of time in the sun – nothing will age you faster.

Top Tip: Homemade firming face mask: whisk an egg white with a tablespoon of honey, a teaspoon of glycerin and enough flour to make a paste, apply to face avoiding the eyes and mouth, leave for ten minutes, then rinse off with warm water. This is great for before a big event as it should reduce the appearance of fine lines for a couple of hours.

Later stage

Whether we have looked after ourselves or not, we will all reach this stage at some point. In later stage skin, collagen production is slowing down, and you will notice the skin becoming less elastic, making the pores expand. As oestrogen levels decline, there will also be a big drop in moisture retention, leading to dehydration and wrinkles. A life of having been exposed to chemicals, polluted environments, air-conditioned and centrally-heated offices and homes, the sun, stress, hormones, less than nutritious diets and less than optimum amounts of exercise will have taken their toll on the skin leaving it tired, fragile and possibly pigmented.

Having said that, it is very important to remember, however, that it is our behaviour and outlook that are 75 per cent responsible for how people perceive our age, and also that you can wipe years of your face by having a more positive mental outlook. Changing a frown to a smile gets rid of some wrinkles instantly! And of course, it's never too late to start taking positive action to save your skin.

- If you have been using a foaming or bar cleanser, it's time to switch, to either a water-soluble creamy cleanser, or a mild, oil-based cleanser to avoid stripping the skin of any of its natural oil and moisture. If you are worried about too much oily residue, you can remove it gently with a damp cloth.
- Because the cells are regenerating much more slowly now, exfoliation is really important both for removing the dulling dead skin cells from the surface, and for helping to regenerate as many new skin cells as possible. Be gentle though, because later stage skin can be quite thin.
- Moisturize regularly – the collagen and elastin under the skin's surface are retaining less moisture, so we need to provide it artificially. Go for something rich and nourishing that will keep the skin supple, plumped-up and well hydrated. Combine with a lightweight moisturizing serum to boost the skin's moisture-retaining capacity.

- If you are going to spend any time at all out doors, it is best for your skin if you wear a daily sunscreen, SPF 15 minimum. It won't turn back the clock, but it will definitely slow it down. Sun damage and sunscreens are explained in more detail in Chapter 1 in the section on the sun (page 13).

- Put a stop to any more free radical damage by going for as much antioxidant action as possible. Look for moisturizers that specifically mention antioxidant vitamins, and increase your intake of antioxidant-packed fresh fruits and vegetables. These are listed in more detail in the section on free radicals (page 7).

- Having wrinkles doesn't mean that you can't have healthy-looking and glowing skin. To enhance the work done with your exfoliating, try using a radiance-boosting cream. This can either be a day treatment or a night treatment. They both work on a cellular level to support the skin cells' own regeneration. The day cream also contains light-reflective particles to give the illusion of increased luminosity in the skin.

- Cut down on smoking. Nicotine stops the body from being able to absorb vitamin C properly, which is not only one of the skin's best sources of radiance but it also means that the body can't produce as much collagen, which only leads to more wrinkles.

Skin-care extras

Banishing blemishes

As mentioned in the section on acne, most spots or pimples are a small infection caused by bacteria that is trapped in the skin. Spots appear red and full of pus as a result of the body's white blood cells fighting off the infection. Squeezing and poking can lead to scarring and isn't recommended. The most sensible thing is to tackle the cause first and then the symptoms.

Cause

Try and figure out what is causing the breakout to see if you can stop it from either getting worse, or continually coming back. Examples of things that could be aggravating the skin and causing it to break out are:

- A new hairstyle – sometimes when hair touches the face, it encourages more oil to be produced, which can result in spots. After a while the skin usually adapts. Keeping the hair clean and not touching the face too much should reduce the amount of extra oil.

- Watch out for things like friction from collars, backpacks and helmets worn too tight as these can also trigger breakouts. The best solution is to find an alternative way to wear or carry the offending articles.
- Any sort of detox can temporarily result in the body getting rid of toxins in the form of spots, and should clear up pretty quickly.
- A change in your routine can also lead to over-production of oil, or a detox reaction. Once you settle, so should your skin.
- Stress is a common cause of breakouts, so try to take steps to reduce the amount of stress in your life. For more advice on this please see the section on stress in Chapter 1.
- Using inappropriate skin care for your skin type is a common cause of breakouts, this is easily rectified by following the advice in this chapter.
- Certain ingredients in skin care and make-up can cause breakouts. This is explained in more detail in the ingredients decoder section (page 105).
- Hormonal changes are also a major cause of spots. This is very hard to control and is more a question of managing the symptoms.
- Certain drugs and medication can lead to breakouts, but this usually clears up once the course is finished.
- Exposure to certain environments can trigger breakouts in certain people e.g. pollution, dust, air conditioning and central heating. Sometimes this exposure is unavoidable and managing the symptoms will be the best that you can do.
- Your genes could mean that you have inherited acne from one of your parents, in which case you should consult your GP for more advice on how to treat it.

Dealing with the symptoms
- Cleanse with a gentle pH balanced cleanser that is both soap- and oil-free.
- If the breakout is mild, gently exfoliate to get rid of any dirt and grime on the skin's surface that can clog the pores and cause breakouts.
- If you are having a major breakout, stay away from scrubs altogether as they can damage the inflamed skin around the spots causing bacteria to spread.
- If you like using toner, use something very mild and soothing, as anything containing alcohol or harsh astringents will dry the skin out too much, causing it to produce even more oil.

- Reduce the redness by holding an ice cube wrapped in a flannel on the red patch for ten minutes. In extreme cases, taking an anti-inflammatory tablet can help, but please make sure that you follow the instructions on the packet carefully and consult your GP or pharmacist first if you are taking any other medication.

- Dab a small amount of a blemish treatment directly onto the blemishes – something with salicylic acid or benzoyl peroxide – and allow five minutes to absorb.

> Top Tip: If you don't have any spot treatment to hand, a crushed aspirin mixed into a paste with a couple of drops of water can have a similar effect, since one of the main ingredients in aspirin is salicylic acid. (Do not do this if you are allergic to aspirin though.) Alternatively, a dab of old-fashioned, no-frills white toothpaste will also do the trick.

- Moisturize with an oil-free moisturizer

Erasing eye issues

The structure of the skin is slightly different around the eye area, it has much less support and its layers are three times thinner than the rest of the face. This means that it dehydrates quicker, it ages quicker, it becomes sensitive more easily and it is the first area to show signs of stress and fatigue. The three major issues in the eye area and the way that the skin shows that it is stressed are dark circles, puffiness and fine lines. If you are unlucky enough to be suffering from all three issues, trying to treat all three at once might not actually help much, because products that help each of these issues individually tend to work against each other. The best thing to do is to deal with the one that is bothering you the most first, and then once that is getting better, deal with the next one. Also, as with blemishes, it is most sensible to look at the causes first, and then the symptoms.

Dark circles

Causes Dark circles that are not genetically inherited can be either a result of poor circulation, lack of nutrition (especially vitamin K), toxic overdose in the diet, lack of sleep, allergies or hormonal imbalances.

Dealing with the symptoms Products containing vitamin K can help.

> Top Tip: You can also boost vitamin K levels by eating more foods that contain it, like turnip greens, broccoli, cabbage, cauliflower, lettuce, soyabean, spinach and liver.

Night-time products containing retinol can also help to minimize dark circles by thickening the skin around the eyes. But use with care – maybe try only every third night for the first week or two. Read the instructions carefully and make sure that you are wearing sun protection in the day time as retinol can increase the skin's sensitivity to sunlight. There is more information about retinol in the ingredients decoder (page 105).

Puffiness

Causes Puffy eyes that are not genetically inherited are usually a result of fluid retention. Salty foods can cause the body to retain water, but also the body tends to hold onto more fluid as a result of it being dehydrated. This happens most often as a result of drinking too much alcohol.

> Top Tip: If you often wake up with puffy eyes, try sleeping with a thicker pillow under your head, and avoid eating salty foods at night.

Dealing with the symptoms Eye creams to 'de-puff' often contain caffeine and work by slightly dehydrating the skin, thus lessening its puffy appearance. Other ingredients to look for are: camomile or arnica and are often labelled 'anti-inflammatory'.

> Top Tip: If you are going to be wearing make-up, wait until after you have applied your concealer to gently apply your de-puffing product. It will work better this way.

Alternatively, if you have time in the morning, place cool compresses on the eyes: slices of cucumber, an ice cube wrapped in a flannel, or even just cotton wool pads soaked in cool water. The coolness diminishes puffiness by constricting the blood vessels. Another way to do this is to apply tea bags that have been soaked in boiling water and then left to cool (regular or camomile work well) because they contain ingredients that also restrict the blood flow which reduces puffiness.

Or, a facial massage like the one detailed later in this chapter (pages 98–105) will boost the lymphatic drainage of the face and therefore ease puffiness. The way that the lymphatic system works is explained in more detail in Chapter 1, in the section on balancing the ingredients (page 4).

Fine lines

Causes Fine lines around the eyes can be caused by any combination of gravity, age, stress, expressiveness, sun damage, smoking, excessive alcohol, environmental conditions, illness, medications and poor nutrition. Many of these things we can bring under control and into balance by making changes to our lifestyle. Most of them are ingredients in the beauty 'cake', explained in more detail in Chapter 1.

Dealing with the symptoms Look for an anti-ageing eye cream that hydrates and puffs up the skin. Ingredients to look for are hyaluronic acid, urea, or vitamins C and E. At night you can try an AHA or retinol treatment, as they soften fine lines. If you haven't used a retinol product before, ease yourself into them, maybe trying only every third night for the first week or two. Read the instructions carefully and make sure that you are wearing sun protection in the daytime as retinol can increase the skin's sensitivity to sunlight. For more information about retinol and other active ingredients, please refer to the ingredients decoder later in this chapter (page 105).

> Top Tip: If your skin condition is predominantly oily, but you are dry and have fine lines around the eye area, just use eye cream at night-time.

How to use eye cream

Specialist eye creams are not just a way for us to spend more money on skin care. Because the skin around the eye is much thinner than the rest of the face, eye creams are much lighter in texture than face creams, and face creams can often be far too rich and heavy for the delicate eye area. Sometimes, the cause of puffiness around the eye can be a result of a build-up of heavy moisturizer residue.

- Choose a cream for the symptom that you wish to deal with first.
- Use eye cream sparingly – you don't need more than three or four small dots below the eye.

figure 2.3 dab eye cream with middle finger

- Use your middle finger to dab the product around the eyes, being careful not to go too close to the lashes. Don't use your index finger, as you are more likely to stretch or drag the skin (see Figure 2.3).
- Be careful not to go too close to the inner corner of the eyes, as this can cause irritation.

Top Tip: To make eye creams and gels feel more soothing, you can store them in the fridge.

Caring for chapped lips

Like the skin around the eyes, the lips are also very delicate. They don't have any sebaceous glands so they don't have the protective barrier that the rest of the face has. This is explained in more detail at the beginning of this section, but it basically means that the lips are therefore much more prone to dehydration and chapping. They also don't have any melanin pigments to protect them from the sun, which makes them extremely vulnerable to sun damage.

All the things that can cause our skin to become dehydrated, like air conditioning, central heating, smoking and sun exposure, also cause our lips to become dehydrated. Most of us will naturally lick our lips when they start to feel dry and instead of making the problem better, this actually makes it worse. This is because when this 'licked' wetness evaporates, it robs the lips of even more moisture. Lips that are chapped not only need moisture, but they also need something to seal it in. It is a three-step process.

Step 1: prepare

Exfoliating the lips not only gets rid of all the dry, flaky bits of skin, but also prepares them to absorb as much moisture as possible. Make sure you include your lips when you are exfoliating the rest of your face. Scrubs and AHAs work just as well on the lips to help improve their texture and boost circulation. Alternatively, try a lip mask made of mashed papaya: papaya contains exfoliating enzymes and can help to soften and refine lip lines. Leave on for 10 to 15 minutes and rinse off with warm water.

> Top Tip: I often have to put make-up on clients who have dry or chapped lips, and lipstick looks so much better on lips that are smooth and non-flaky. The way I deal with this problem is to massage a bit of rich moisturizer or lip balm into them with a soft toothbrush – baby ones are great for this.

Step 2: hydrate

Keep lips hydrated from the inside by drinking two litres of water a day and eating plenty of fluid-packed fruits and vegetables like melon, grapefruit, strawberries, broccoli, cabbage, cauliflower, celery, aubergine, lettuce, bell peppers, radish, spinach, courgettes and tomatoes.

> Top Tip: When applying moisturizer to your face, apply it to your lips as well – there isn't much point in applying the next step of lip balm to seal moisture in if there isn't any there to seal in, in the first place!

Step 3: seal

Lips need a thick balm to seal in the moisture and stop it from evaporating, and it needs to contain SPF 15 if you are going to be outside in the sun. This balm acts as a barrier against all the things that can damage, and keeps the lips soft and smooth whether they are left like this or as a good base for make-up.

> Top Tip: For touch-ups during the day, have a small tube of moisturizer in your handbag – freebie samples are great for this – so that you can continue the layering effect, for maximum moisture and luscious lips.

Fixing facial hair

Facial hair appears either as a result of genetics or hormonal activity. Marilyn Monroe's face was covered in downy blonde baby hair – which is credited with being one of the reasons that she was so photogenic, as all the little soft hairs acted like a light diffuser, softening the focus and blurring any imperfections. If this is you, I would advise leaving your facial hair alone, as messing with it might lead to it all getting thicker and more visible.

If, on the other hand, you have a few stray hairs here and there you want to get rid of, do it at the same time as you do your eyebrows, either by tweezing, waxing, threading, epilating or dissolving. For more information on facial hair removal tips, please refer to the eyebrows section of this chapter (page 132). I wouldn't shave them because that creates hair with a blunt edge, which leaves it looking much darker and coarser than if it were to re-grow from scratch again. On the upper lip, the hairs can be really tiny and plucking may not be realistic – waxing or depilation might be a better option. If you don't want to get rid of them, then you could try a facial bleaching cream. Be very careful when using bleaching creams and be sure to read the instructions properly first.

> Top Tip: Plan to wax any facial hair the day before a date or a special event, just in case you end up with a bit of redness.

Face massage

Working as a make-up artist, it is my job to make people look their best. It can sometimes be a challenge to make up models or actors if they are stressed and exhausted from either heavy work schedules or if they have just come straight from a long-haul flight, because the best faces are ones that are rested and relaxed. Luckily my training as a massage therapist means that I have a secret weapon in the form of a facial massage routine which works on many levels to improve the complexion.

- Because the face is made up of lots of muscles and can therefore hold a lot of tension, relieving that tension also alleviates symptoms of stress in the body. For more information about stress and how it affects the body please refer to the section on stress in Chapter 1 (page 41). When stress is relieved in the body, the results are visible in the face.

- It helps to de-puff the face by stimulating the lymphatic system to transport any stagnant fluids to the lymph nodes to be filtered for toxins. For more information on this please see the section on balancing the ingredients in Chapter 1 (page 4).

- Massaging the face stimulates the blood circulation which brings not only more nourishment but also more colour to the skin.

- Stimulating the surface of the skin acts like an exfoliant because it encourages the skin to shed its dead outer layer, which helps to clear blocked pores while at the same time stimulating new cells to grow, resulting in healthier, more radiant skin. This is explained in more detail at the beginning of this section.

- Exfoliated skin has more capacity to absorb moisturizer and can therefore appear plumper and younger. This is explained in more detail at the beginning of this section.

- Dark circles and puffiness under the eyes can be alleviated by improved circulation. This is explained in more detail at the beginning of this section.

For all these reasons, a facial massage is a great tool to add to your skin-care routine, it is also a great way of dealing with a puffy hangover face, a great anti-ageing strategy and the perfect way to erase sleepy crease lines on the face.

Top Tip: If you are really puffy, massage your face while lying down on your back, as this will help with fluid drainage.

My face massage routine

You will get the most benefit from these movements if you perform them slowly, gently and carefully. The whole routine should take you 10–15 minutes, or you can pick and mix the movements as necessary for specific situations.

> Top Tip: To massage properly, your hands and fingers need to be able to glide smoothly across the skin, so use either a cleanser or a little bit of massage oil and be sure to warm it in your hands first.

1 This can deflate and define puffy and swollen skin

Place little fingers alongside the nose and massage from the centre of the face outwards and upwards in a wave like motion. Make long sweeping movements using the flat of your hands – like body-brushing the face. Do the same at the chin and the forehead – twice in each position.

> Top Tip: If you have had a night out, this is really good to do before you go to sleep because it speeds up the detoxification process.

figure 2.4 face massage step 1

2 This can release tension in the jaw

The jaw muscle is one of the strongest muscles in the whole body and stores a lot of body energy and therefore a lot of tension. Place fingers under jaw and chin and gently press and release along the line of the jaw – back and forth three times.

figure 2.5 face massage step 2

3 This can relieve tension headaches, reduce hyperactivity and help to improve memory

Using your middle or index fingers, do clockwise circles to the temples, slowly and with a little bit of pressure. Do this for 30 seconds to a minute.

figure 2.6 face massage step 3

4 This can improve alertness and help relieve dizziness and nausea
This one also smoothes and helps to prevent wrinkles by improving muscle tone at the corners of the mouth as well as bringing a healthy glow to the cheeks. Start with the tips of the index fingers midway between the nose and the middle of upper lip, press gently and then stroke from here to just over the corners of the mouth, applying pressure the whole time, then moving under the cheekbones, to the top of the ear, following the crease where the ear is attached to the head and behind the earlobe following the bony bump. Repeat five times.

figure 2.7 face massage step 4

5 This can help with asthma and bronchial congestion

Place the left hand to left side of top of head, right index finger just above the flare of the nostril, small circles here, then follow the stroke as in step 4. Repeat on the other side, and do three times each side in total.

figure 2.8 face massage step 5

6 This can help to relieve sinus congestion and sinusitis, eye-strain and the congestion that causes bags to form under the eyes

Same hand position as step 5, find the bone that is half way up the side of the nostril and do small circular massage movements at a point just right of the nose, then follow the stroke as in step 4. Repeat on the other side and do three times each side in total.

figure 2.9 face massage step 6

7 This can relieve tired eyes, improve the skin tone around the eyes and help relieve bags and dark circles

Same hand position as step 5, with the right index finger just below inner corner of the right eye apply gentle pressure. Move slowly along the bony surface of the eye socket, applying pressure all the way along. End at the outer corner of the eye between the bone of the eye socket and the eyeball and press gently here. Repeat three times each side in total.

figure 2.10 face massage step 7

8 **This can help detoxify the liver and relieve headaches due to eye strain**

This works by increasing energy to the eye socket, nose and centre part of the face and stimulates pressure points that drain toxins away from your eye area. Start with both index fingers at the tip of the nose, stroke up the midline of the nose all the way to the top and branch out to either side to the point where the eyebrows begin on the upper bony surface that forms the eye socket. Continue along the upper ridge of the socket applying pressure throughout. End at the temples. Repeat five times.

figure 2.11 face massage step 8

9 **This can release tension throughout the body and help to nourish and relax the nervous system**

Starting at the inner end of each eyebrow, pinch along the eyebrow to its outer edge. Use your thumb and index finger in a rolling motion – pinch and roll the index finger over the thumb and then roll the thumb over the index finger. Repeat five times.

figure 2.12 face massage step 9

10 This can relieve headaches, relax and invigorate the forehead muscles and stimulate energy

This works by stimulating the deep centres of the brain and helps to balance the body both mentally and physically. Using a 'shampoo' action – small circular movements over the whole scalp, slowly and with a bit of pressure. Make sure to cover the whole scalp and hairline. Do this for about one minute.

figure 2.13 face massage step 10

Ingredients decoder

Finding the right skin care for your skin condition and stage will sometimes involve you needing to find products that contain the right ingredients. Reading an ingredients label can sometimes leave you feeling more confused than you were to begin with. Here I am going to attempt to decode some of the most common terms and ingredients.

As I mentioned earlier, the most expensive products are not necessarily the best ones, and mass market products are generally pretty good quality and will work fine for most people. What you are paying for in the more expensive brands, apart from luxury packaging, should be a higher concentration of active ingredients (the ingredients that do more than just cleanse or moisturize). When the concentration of a certain ingredient is high, then it features higher in the ingredients list. So this is the first place you should look to find out what a product will actually do.

Terms: what do they actually mean?

- *Alcohol-free* This should mean that the product is free from drying alcohols, such as benzyl alcohol, methyl alcohol, methanol, ethyl (grain) alcohol, or ethanol – often listed as SD alcohol. There are, however, some alcohols that aren't drying. These are fatty alcohols, such as cetyl, stearyl and cetearyl alcohol, which are all widely used as emollients and emulsifiers.

- *Binding agents* Hold products together and prevent the separation of the water and oil components.

- *Comedogenic* A comedone is the medical term for a spot or a blocked pore, therefore an ingredient that is comedogenic, is one that is highly likely to block pores and cause spots. It will most definitely aggravate any spots, and should be avoided by anyone who has acne-prone skin. Sally Penford, Education Manager at the International Dermal Institute, warns that in high percentages, any of these ingredients can be comedogenic:

  - acetylated lanolin
  - butyl stearate
  - cocoa butter
  - flax oil
  - isoparraffin C9-11
  - isoproyl myristate
  - linseed oil
  - myristyl myristate
  - myreth-3 myristate
  - octyl palmitate
  - octyl stearate.

- *Dermatologist tested* This literally means that the product has been tested by a dermatologist. The results may or may not have been scientifically valid or medically approved.

- *Emollients* These are substances that smooth and soften the skin.

- *Fragrance-free* This doesn't necessarily mean that the product won't smell of anything. It will generally mean that no perfume has been added to the product. Some of the ingredients may have a natural scent.

- *Hypoallergenic* This means that the product has been specifically formulated to contain fewer irritants. If you have very sensitive skin, check the ingredients list to make sure.

- *Humectant* A humectant is any substance that can attract water, usually out of the air. By definition, all humectants are also moisturizers.
- *Natural* This can be misleading, as there is often a massive difference between one manufacturer's definition of 'natural' and another's. It should mean that the ingredients come from natural as opposed to synthetic sources, but people can use the term even if it is only a minute quantity. Natural doesn't always mean better, either – some botanical extracts including mints and citruses can actually be irritating, while their synthetic counterparts can be far more effective.
- *Oil-free* Even if a product doesn't contain any ingredients specifically called 'oil', it still might have other waxy or oily components, that you might want to avoid, especially if you have oily or acne-prone skin. Lanolin (technically a wax) is often used in oil-free products, and can be one of the worst things that you can put on top of oily skin (see below).

Top Tip: If you want to test a product out, do the oil migration test. Smear a bit of the product on a sheet of white paper and wait 24 hours. Then, hold the paper up to the light and notice the ring of oil that has migrated around the cosmetic. The bigger the ring the more oil the product contains!

- *Preservatives* These are substances that kill bacteria, yeasts and/or moulds, thus preventing spoilage. Preservatives are not bad things to have in cosmetics.
- *Surfactants* These are substances that enable a product to easily spread and glide across the skin.

Common problem ingredients

- *Alcohol* Alcohol is very drying. It strips the skin of its natural barrier protection, and can dehydrate it. This can cause blockages under the surface and lead to damaged collagen under the surface. An alternative is bio-enhanced grapefruit-seed extract.
- *Artificial fragrance* Synthetic fragrances are made from over 200 chemicals and can often be responsible for skin irritation and in some cases can even cause memory impairment. Alternatives include essential oils and natural fragrances (although even these can hold problems for fragrance sensitive people).

- *Drug and cosmetic pigments (also known as D&C dyes)*
  Some drug and cosmetic red dyes can be comedogenic. This
  is because they are coal tar derivatives. Ever since doctors
  noticed that acne was an occupational hazard of chimney
  sweeps, coal tar has been known for its acne-causing
  properties. Alternatives include annatto, cochineal powder,
  caramel, guanine, iron oxides and grape-skin.

- *Isopropyl myristate* This is used in cosmetics because it
  makes them easy to apply; it feels silky and sheer. It is the
  main ingredient in WD40, which is used to lubricate rusty
  locks. It also has a life of its own: if you left some isopropyl
  myristate overnight in a cup, some of it would actually creep
  over the top of the cup and down the sides and onto the table-
  top. In the skin, it can creep into follicles and cause irritation,
  resulting in congestion. It is a very aggressive chemical
  substance and in cosmetic products it can be the cause of lids
  cracking and mirrors in compacts becoming unglued.
  Alternatives include plant oils (except coconut), kalaya oil,
  vegetable glycerine, propylene glycol, polyethylene glycol and
  butylene glycol.

- *Lanolin* Lanolin is one of the most common ingredients in
  cosmetics. Lanolin is oil extracted from sheep's wool.
  Prolonged use can result in the skin becoming more sensitive.
  It can cause congestion in the form of tiny blockages beneath
  the surface of the skin, which can be felt with the fingertips,
  called milia. Alternatives include plant oils (except coconut),
  kalaya oil, vegetable glycerine, propylene glycol, polyethylene
  glycol and butylene glycol.

- *Mineral oil* This is a by-product of petroleum. It is used in
  cosmetic products mostly because it is cheap and certain
  grades of it can be comedogenic. It forms a good barrier, but
  it doesn't allow the skin to breathe or get rid of toxins. It can
  also decrease the ability of the cells to exchange nutrients.
  Milia (as mentioned under lanolin, above) can be common
  around the eyes and mouth as a result of mineral oils in
  cosmetics. Alternatives include plant oils (except coconut),
  kalaya oil, vegetable glycerine, propylene glycol, polyethylene
  glycol and butylene glycol

- *Paraffin wax* Is often used in moisturizers, but non-food
  grade paraffin wax may contain oils and other impurities
  which may be toxic or harmful. Alternatives include
  beeswax, jojoba wax, carnauba wax and candelilla wax.

- *Petrolatum* Petolatum is a refined form of mineral oil and is
  the basis of petroleum jelly. It acts as a good barrier but can

limit the skin's ability to function and can also cause congestion in the form of milia (see lanolin above). In some people it can cause oversensitivity to sunlight. Alternatives include beeswax, jojoba wax, carnauba wax and candelilla wax.

Active ingredients

Many ingredients in skin care can do our skin a lot of good though. These are usually known as 'active ingredients', and include things like:

- *Alpha hydroxy acids or AHAs* These are naturally occurring acids, derived from the sugars in particular plants. The most common are lactic acid, glycolic acid, citric acid and malic acid, which naturally occur in milk, sugar cane, citrus fruits and apples respectively. They work by dissolving the 'glue' that holds dead skin cells together, which exfoliates the skin and speeds up the skin's natural cell renewal process. They can be used to improve the appearance of fine lines, pigmentation and acne and they can increase the tone, texture, smoothness and softness of the skin resulting in an overall healthy glow. Start out gently to make sure that your skin isn't sensitive.
- *Arbutin* See kojic acid (below).
- *Betaglucan* This is derived from oats and is a superior moisturizer as well as having powerful antioxidant properties. It forms an invisible film over the skin and helps the skin to retain moisture. When used in cosmetics and skin-care products it can relieve skin itching, irritation and inflammation, moisturize extremely dry skin, soothe sensitive skin, reduce the discomfort of sunburn, relieve itching, and can also be used to cleanse skin.
- *Beta hydroxy acid, BHA, or salicylic acid* Salicylic acid is a naturally-occurring acid derived from willow bark, wintergreen leaves and sweet birch bark. It is also one of the main ingredients in aspirin. It works in the same way as AHAs (above) to exfoliate dead skin cells, but as a BHA, salicylic acid has antibacterial properties and can also cut though oil which makes it very effective as a blemish and acne treatment. BHAs tend not to be as irritating to sensitive skins as AHAs can.
- *Benzoyl peroxide* This is an anti-bacterial spot treatment that works in pretty much the same way that salicylic acid (above) does. It will make a spot dry out and peel off.
- *Bromelain enzymes* See papain enzymes (below).

- *Citric Acid* See alpha hydroxy acid (above).
- *Glycolic Acid* See alpha hydroxy acid (above).
- *Hyaluronic acid or sodium hyaluronate* This is a natural humectant with excellent water binding capabilities. It is capable of attracting and retaining 1,000 times its own weight in water and used in cosmetics it can help to smooth and refine skin texture.
- *Kojic acid* Kojic acid, arbutin and licorice extract are all naturally occurring substances that are highly regarded for their ability to inhibit the over-production of melanin which leads to pigmentation. Used in conjunction with exfoliation, they are effective skin lighteners.
- *L-ascorbic acid (also known as sodium ascorbyl phosphate or vitamin-C)* This is the form that vitamin C must be in so that the body can absorb it through the skin. Vitamin C is a known antioxidant and can therefore protect skin by neutralizing free radicals, which would damage the skin. It also stimulates the production of collagen. As an ingredient in cosmetics it is therefore very good for protecting the skin and also for improving the appearance of fine lines and can give a healthy glow. It works well in synergy or partnership with vitamin E (tochopherol) – they work to protect each other from free radical damage.
- *Lactic acid* Lactic acid is a natural humectant and has a larger molecule size than glycolic acid, which can make it less irritating. See alpha hydroxy acid (above).
- *Licorice extract* See kojic acid (above).
- *Malic acid* See alpha hydroxy acid (above).
- *Panthenol (vitamin B5)* Panthenol is a natural humectant that has reparative properties because it stimulates the production of collagen and elastin. Collagen and elastin are explained in more detail above (pages 59–60). Panthenol comes from the Greek word *panthos*, meaning 'everywhere', and is found in many foods, especially fruits and vegetables.
- *Papain enzymes* Papain and bromelain enzymes come from papaya and pineapple fruits respectively. They work in a similar way to AHAs by utilizing catalytic action to digest and exfoliate dead skin and proteins from the surface of the skin and deep within pores. Using masks containing these enzymes can result in skin that has a much smoother texture and an overall softer and healthier glow. They can be good to use on sensitive skin because they are non-abrasive and gentle.

- *Retinol (also known as retinyl palmitate or vitamin A)* This can visibly improve the appearance of fine lines by stimulating collagen and elastin production. It can lighten brown discoloration by increasing exfoliation and skin cell renewal. It can re-texturize, smoothe, tone, and hydrate the skin resulting in younger-looking, healthier skin cells. It is best to use retinol products at night to make the most of the fact that the skin can absorb more active ingredients while it is going through its own natural repair routine. Using retinol can have side-effects though: it can cause irritation, tingling and redness. If these symptoms persist or you are at all worried, you should stop using the product and check with your GP or skin specialist. Always follow the instructions carefully and avoid extra sensitive areas like eyelids. UV rays from the sun can irritate areas of skin that have been treated with retinol, this is why it is important to make sure that you use sun protection if you are using a retinol product.

- *Salicylic acid* See beta hydroxy acid (above).

- *Sodium ascorbyl phosphate* See L-ascorbic acid (above).

- *Sodium hyaluronate* See hyaluronic acid (above).

- *Tochopherol (also known as tocopheryl acetate or vitamin E)* This is a natural humectant that can help to smoothe skin and repair its natural barrier function. It works well in synergy or partnership with vitamin C (L-ascorbic acid) – they protect each other from free radical damage.

- *Vitamin A* See retinol (above).

- *Vitamin B5* See panthenol (above).

- *Vitamin-C* See L-ascorbic acid (above).

- *Vitamin E* See tochopherol (above).

Good sunscreen ingredients

- *Chemical – avobenzone or parsol 1789* This is the best UVA absorber, it screens out 80 per cent UVA. UVA is divided into two subsets: UVA 2–320–340nm and UVA1–340–400nm. UVA1 can cause deeper damage as it penetrates deeper into the dermis. Most sunscreens screen only UVA2, but avobenzone also screen UVA1.

- *Physical – titanium dioxide* This provides superior protection from both UVA and UVB rays. It will not irritate skin or eyes like some chemical agents. It works by partially blocking UV radiation by scattering or reflecting its energy rays. Modern preparations are not as chalky as they were in the past. It is organic and therefore more environmentally friendly.

> *Note:* If you are at all in doubt about anything to do with your skin or the ingredients in products, speak to a dermatologist – British Association of Dermatologists 0207 383 0266.

Make-up *(as needed or desired)*

Even though I work as a make-up artist and I make my living by putting make-up on people, I still maintain that in terms of beauty, it really is just the icing on the cake, and that if the cake is good in the first place, then little or no icing is all you need. It isn't healthy to rely on your make-up as the benchmark of your own beauty. It is really important to remember that beauty comes from within and that make-up is a tool that you can use to enhance that beauty. Make-up should be something that you can use to highlight who you are, not something to hide behind.

However, changing how we look can have a massive impact not only on how we see ourselves, but also on how people around us respond to us. If our skin is behaving badly, we all have the tendency to feel negative towards ourselves. When we feel negative about ourselves, it changes the way that we relate to other people, which in turn changes the way that they relate to us. These are the times when make-up can be an amazing tool. A bit of enhancement here and a bit of concealing there together with some strategic shading and highlighting can result in us being able to see ourselves in a much more positive way. This in turn makes for a more positive atmosphere in general. A positive attitude and a healthy dose of self-esteem are two of the main ingredients in the recipe for our beauty 'cake'. So, make-up, even though it is just the icing, can also play its part in the actual cake recipe by boosting levels of self-esteem and happiness.

I like to think about make-up as if it were medicine. It can be a fantastic 'pick-me-up', creating an instant healthy glow. It can act like a 'pain killer', getting rid of spots and blemishes in an instant. It can raise levels of excitement, putting a flush in the cheeks and colour on the lips. It can even work like an aphrodisiac, painting on irresistibly smoky 'come-to-bed' eyes. And used carefully, wisely and in moderation, it can be a great asset to any modern woman's life. Like medicine, the important thing to remember is not to rely on it too much. When we rely on medicine too much, our own body stops being able to defend itself, and we start to become dependant on it. When we start to become too dependent on make-up, we can lose sight of who we really are. Don't forget that the real key to beauty is in learning to accept ourselves.

For me, the best make-up is make-up that you don't notice straight away: when you see someone and the first thing you think is 'Wow! You look great today!', not 'Wow! Great make-up!' The kind of make-up where you look in the mirror and you see yourself staring back, but it's just a better version of yourself. Sometimes you just need to change the way you think about your make-up. Giving yourself a glowing complexion to make yourself look more rested and awake is a much better idea than covering your skin behind a mask of foundation. Cleverly placing colour on your face to give it dimension and energy, or defining your eyes to make them appear brighter and clearer is much better than trying to look like somebody else.

Look at your face and try to really see what is there. Stop yourself from wishing that you looked different, because this will stop you from being able to see what is actually there. Getting to know your face, its shape, how it reacts to products and light is the best make-up tool that you can have. Once you really understand your own face, the simplest of make-up tricks will give you the power to make the most of your best features, thus detracting attention from your least favourite. Everything that I know about make-up is included in this book, so once you know your face, you should also have all the knowledge that you need to be your own make-up artist.

Make-up bag make-over

Being your own make-up artist starts with having the right kit. Follow these steps and you will have a purpose-built professional style make-up kit that is just for you.

1 Have a clear-out

In the same way that we said that it is much better to clean up the kitchen before we bake a cake, this is a bit like a detox for your make-up bag. Lay out all your products and ask yourself these questions: Do I use it? Do I need it? Do I love it?

• If you have a bunch of products that all do the same thing, keep the one you use the most, and give or throw the others away.

- If you haven't used a product in the last year, bin it.
- Get rid of anything that is broken or squashed, leaking or held together with sticky tape.
- Get rid of anything that is past its use-by date (see below) or has changed texture, colour or smells funny.
- Finally, discard any brushes, puffs and sponges that are over-used and/or falling apart.

Use-by dates

Foundation	1–2 years
Concealer	1 year
Powder	2 years
Mascara	3 months
Lipstick	1–2 years
Lip/eye pencil	1 year
Eye shadow	1–2 years
Powder blush	2 years
Cream blush	1 year

How to get the most out of your products

- Keep the lids on things when you are not using them.
- Use only cotton buds, clean brushes and clean fingers to touch your products.
- Keep them cool (e.g. out of direct sunlight).

2 Give everything a clean

Wash both make-up bag and your brushes, puffs and sponges (if they are in a really bad way, treat yourself to new ones and then try to keep them clean!). Clean your brushes once a month, washing them with a conditioning baby shampoo, then drying them flat, letting the bristles hang over the edge of a table or shelf so that the air can circulate. Wipe out your bag regularly with an antibacterial wipe, which is also handy for cleaning around the tops of any gunky lids. Puffs should be washed once a week, and sponges should be washed out each time they are used.

> Top Tip: Have a spare puff which can be used while the other is drying.

I can't stress enough how important make-up hygiene is: all these tools and products are going on your face – there is no point spending time and money on skin care and cleaning dirt and germs off your face if you are just going to wipe germs and dirt on with your makeup. Also remember that we use make-up around our eyes, which are two of the most sensitive parts of our whole bodies. I am ultra-fanatical about keeping my kit clean and not using the same brushes on more than one client unless they have been cleaned first. I would advise you to only share brushes, lipstick or mascara with someone that you would also share a toothbrush with!

> Top Tip: Go for a compact make-up bag – the smaller the bag the less likely you are to fill it up with unneccessary items.

3 Get your tools right

You might be thinking that buying extra brushes is a bit over the top, but using good tools takes away a lot of the effort in good make-up application. I am a professional and it would definitely be a challenge for me to do a great make-up on someone if I was only allowed to use the brushes that were provided with the make-up – usually they are too small to have enough control over the finish that you get. Don't throw them away though, because they can be handy for through the day touch-ups. The following list contains everything that you might need if you want to give your make-up a professional finish at home.

My top tools

1 *A good pair of tweezers* To make tweezing stray hairs much quicker and easier. This is explained in more detail in the easy eyebrows section (page 132).
2 *A pair of eyelash curlers* To open and accentuate the eyes. Instructions on how to use eyelash curlers are included in the eyelash enhancing section (page 160).
3 *Sponge or foundation brush* If you don't like using your fingers, use whatever you like the feel of best. Applying foundation with a damp sponge will give you a more sheer coverage than if you use a dry one. Foundation brushes are great for blending more than one shade together and can also give a nice sheer finish. I prefer to use my fingers because I feel that the heat from my hands makes it easier to blend the foundation into the skin. This is purely down to personal preference. Don't forget to keep your sponges and foundation brushes clean.
4 *Concealer brushes* A flat-tipped one for under the eyes, for sheer, even application, and a small pointy one for blemishes (it has to be small in order to 'retouch' the blemish as opposed to simply drawing attention to it!) Synthetic ones are usually better.

5 *Decent-sized bronzer and blusher brushes* The small ones that often come in the packets are often too small to get good coverage and easy blending. Bigger, fluffier ones give a more even and subtle finish.

6 *Eye shadow brushes* My personal favourites are a fat one to wash colour over the whole eyelid, a pointier one for definition, a regular-sized one for applying highlighter, a stiffer one for blending and a flatter one for applying creams or glosses.

7 *Brow-and-lash grooming brushes* A wand-like brow-grooming brush for brushing stray hairs into place, and a stiff-angled eyebrow brush for applying powder for definition (if you are not using a pencil); also an eyelash comb or brow-grooming brush can be used to comb out eye lashes.

8 *An eyeliner brush* A slanted flat one is the easiest for painting lines with and can be used either with gel eyeliner, or dampened and used with eyeshadow.

9 *A lip brush* For precision application – it is easier to control how much colour goes on the lips and it is much easier to get into the corners.

10 *Powder applicators* Either a large, soft, fluffy powder brush, preferably made with natural fibres, or a soft powder puff. Powder is very important for a flawless, shine-free finish and applying it with a brush will give a much more lightweight and sheer finish, great for natural, barely there make-up looks. Applying with a powder puff leaves much more powder on the face and is good for setting make-up that has to stay on for a long time, or for a look that is a bit more sophisticated or dramatic. It can also be handy for oily skin conditions as the pad can soak up any excess oil while applying powder to set the make-up.

Top Tip: A good brush should feel soft (*never* scratchy) on the skin and the bristles shouldn't fall out easily.

On top of these tools, you also need:

• *Tissues and cotton buds* Essential both for application and for cleaning up.

• *A pencil sharpener* To keep your pencils sharp and clean.

• *A decent mirror* Working in a compact mirror is fine for touch-ups and emergencies, but you get a much better overall view in a *clean* mirror that you can stand back from.

- *Good light* Light can make a big difference to how you see your face. I always prefer to work in daylight and often set up in front of a window if I can. Make-up applied in natural daylight looks good under any lighting conditions. But as this isn't always possible, it is important to be aware that:
  - yellow light absorbs red so you may end up applying too much blusher (yellow lighting is often used in hotels as it is soft, warm and welcoming)
  - green light makes most people look really unwell (think aeroplane toilet!)
  - light from above creates shadows under your eyes that you will then try to cover – counteract by trying to keep your chin up
  - light from the side tends to over-emphasize any blemishes, which might make you apply too much concealer.

4 Create your 'capsule collection' of the basic products

Base basics

When I talk to people about make-up, it seems pretty universal: most people have some sort of an issue with foundation. It seems to have earned itself a bit of a reputation and a lot of people are either a bit scared off by thinking it will look like a mask or they can't be bothered with faffing around with it, or they are simply too overwhelmed by the choices and so they just forget about it.

If your skin isn't perfectly smooth, hydrated, even in colour, and blemish free, then foundation can be the key to making the rest of the world think that it is!

In the same way that the foundations of a house are what make it stable, a good foundation is the key to great make-up. It should never look like a mask, if it does, then you have applied too much. Think of it as a tool that you can use to beautify the look of your skin by using it to even out tone and texture. Blemishes and problem areas are dealt with using concealer, not layer upon layer of foundation, the ultimate aim being to have as little product on your face that can still give the illusion of perfection. This is all down to clever application.

Many modern foundations are made to work together with your skin-care routine and contain all sorts of active ingredients, and most of them sell themselves as being sheer, light-weight and natural looking because the idea of cakey thick make-up is simply unattractive. In this section, I shall try to make the world of foundations a little simpler and help you along your way to creating perfect-looking skin.

Types of foundation

- *Tinted moisturizers* are great for people who just don't like the feel of anything on their skin. Tinted moisturizers are very lightweight but have just enough tint in them to even out skin tone and give a healthy glow.

> Top Tip: Tinted moisturizers are perfect for saving time in the morning because you can moisturize and do your base all at the same time. New formulas even contain sunscreen, so that kills three birds with one stone!

- *Liquid foundations* are the next step up from tinted moisturizer. They will generally give a little bit more coverage than a tinted moisturizer, but this can vary according to how it is applied. Sometimes liquids can 'separate' slightly, especially if left to stand for long periods, so its always worth giving them a shake before using. Formulations that are specifically 'long wear' can tend to feel a bit heavier on the skin.

> Top Tip: You can sometimes get away with using the old, thick, foundation that is in the top of the lid as concealer.

- *Mousse foundations* tend to be very lightweight, have a more matt finish and are easy to apply.
- *Cream, compact cream and stick foundations* are generally thicker in consistency and provide more coverage. On skins that aren't oily, they can sometimes also double as concealer.
- *Compact powder foundations* are a mixture of foundation and powder all in one. They can be quite dry and are usually matt in texture. They are very easy to use and do pretty much stay put, but they can sometimes feel a little heavier on the skin.

> Top Tip: If you are someone who does their make-up on the go (e.g. on the train or bus – *not* in the car while driving) a compact powder formula is quick and easy and takes away the need to have powder as well.

Four steps to perfect foundation:

1 The texture needs to be right not only for your skin, but also for the purpose: is it for a natural, 'no make-up' look, or is it for a special event where you might be photographed?

2 The finish needs to be right for your skin type and for the look that you are trying to create.

3 The shade needs to match your skin colour perfectly.

4 It needs to be applied well.

1 Choosing the right texture

Use your hand to test out textures.

> Top Tip: If your skin looks good without make-up and you just want to even out the skin tone a little, a tinted moisturizer will work for all skin types and all skin stages; or, skip this stage completely and just apply a little concealer to subtly hide any imperfections.

Textures for skin condition:

- *Normal/balanced skin* Any type of foundation can be used on this type of skin.

- *Dry skin* Stay away from compact powder foundations, as the powder will only highlight all your dry flaky bits. Richer and creamier oil-based products are OK for dry skins as they can help to seal in moisture. For light to medium coverage, go for a liquid. For medium to heavy coverage, try a cream, stick or compact foundation.

- *Oily skin* Look for either an oil-free liquid or possibly mousse formulation. If your skin is clear, on oil-free compact powder foundation could work well also. Oil control or mattifying formulas are good for oily skins too because they actually mop up oil as it appears without making your skin look dull.

- *Sensitive skin* Look for a lightweight liquid formula and check the ingredients for fragrance, live plant extracts or lanolin as these could all trigger a reaction from sensitive skin. Avoid anything too rich and creamy, as the oil content could be a problem, as could anything with too many chemicals (some oil-free formulas) or anything too drying (like compact powders). If in doubt, stick with a tinted moisturizer.

- *Acne skin* Avoid anything too rich or oily as the oil content could aggravate your symptoms. Avoid anything too heavy because if not applied really well, formulas with heavy coverage often end up highlighting spots rather than disguising them. Avoid compact formulas because they can hold onto and become a breeding ground for bacteria. That leaves you with the choice between a lightweight liquid formula or a tinted moisturizer.
- *Pigmented skin* Pigmented skin is often dry, so the same rules apply as for dry skin, and it really is more of a question of coverage. I would resist the urge to try to cover pigmented skin too much however, as your make-up can quickly start to look like a mask, which for me is often much worse than no-make up at all.
- *Eczema skin* Eczema skin is often sensitive and dry at the same time, which can make it hard to find products for. It might be a question of trial and error because each person with eczema skin will have different sensitivities. If in doubt, stick with a tinted moisturizer.

Textures for skin stage:

- *Early stage* Any type of foundation is usually OK, but skin condition allowing, I would play up the fact that you have youthful-looking skin by keeping the base sheer and transparent by using a lightweight liquid or a tinted moisturizer or nothing at all.
- *Mid-stage* Avoid compact powder foundations, because if applied too heavily the powder will end up highlighting any fine lines.
- *Later stage* Less is often more with later stage skin. The more product that you put on your face, the more there is to settle in the lines. I would advise either a lightweight liquid foundation or a tinted moisturizer for later-stage skin. If you are also dry and you want to go for something rich and creamy then be sure to apply it sparingly, and as for mid stage, I would avoid compact powder foundations, as the powder will only highlight any wrinkles. If you choose well and apply well, your foundation can make you look much younger.

2 Deciding on the finish

Use your hand to test out finishes. In order to see the finished texture you need to blend a small amount right into your skin. There are three main types of finish:

- *Dewy* This will often have light-reflective particles in it to give the illusion of radiance. It will give the skin a really three-dimensional quality. This can be great for later stage skin as it can soften the appearance of lines and counteract any greyness in the skin. It can be great also if you are going to be photographed as it is a bit like being 'retouched' – the luminosity acts to soften the focus a little. If you are trying to create a look that is pretty and youthful, then I would recommend this finish. Be careful though, because there is quite a fine line between being dewy and shiny – and shiny can end up looking sweaty, which doesn't look great either in real life or in pictures! Don't apply too much and be sure to set with a dusting of powder. Avoid if you have oily skin.

- *Matt* Matt is the opposite of dewy, and evens out skin tone in a very flat, more two-dimensional way. It is good for creating dramatic or sophisticated looks. Matt finishes are often also oil-control or mattifying formulas and are good for oily skins, but can end up being quite dull if you are later-stage. Avoid if you have really dry skin as it could highlight any flaky bits.

- *Satin* I call satin finish any finish that you get from a good application of most foundations that aren't specifically either dewy or matt. It should look even and velvety smooth on the skin, and the skin should just look perfect. This finish works pretty well universally.

> Top Tip: To create a dewy finish with a satin or matt formula, mix a little liquid or cream highlighter/ illuminator with your foundation.

3 Getting the shade right

- Don't test foundation shades on your hand. Hands are very rarely the same colour as faces, and this is where most people go wrong. Ideally, foundation matches the skin on your neck just behind the ear – this guarantees a natural looking finish by ensuring that you don't get a 'tide mark'.

- Shop for foundation without wearing any foundation on your face so that you can make sure that the shade you buy matches your natural skin tone as closely as possible by actually testing it on your bare skin.

- Remember that store lighting can affect how you see the shades, so take a compact mirror with you so that you can walk outside of the store to check what the shades look like on your skin in the daylight.

- Once you have found the texture that you like, chose two or three shades that you think might be correct and blend a small dab of each in stripes across your jaw/cheek (this usually matches the skin on your neck the best). It's best if the stripes don't touch – you will be able to see the difference better. Then go outside to check them in the daylight. If one of them looks like it disappears into your skin, then that is the correct shade for you. If none of them disappear, try again on the other side of your face. If you don't find one after that, you will need to clean your cheeks off and start again. It's worth persevering though, because it doesn't matter how well you apply it, a base that is the wrong colour, always looks like 'make-up'. A well-applied base that is the right colour can be easily mistaken for perfect skin – which is what we are ultimately aiming for.

- Avoid pink-toned foundations at all costs. Yellow-based tones look more natural on everyone.

Top Tip: If your skin is darker you may find that your skin tone is slightly deeper around the edge of your face than it is in the centre. Trying to even this out with one shade can often flatten the face, and it can end up looking either too pale or too dark. My advice is to choose two foundations that match the two different shades and apply them where necessary, blending carefully at the joins. This will keep the dimension in your face and make your base look much more natural.

- If, after all that, you are still in doubt, ask the sales assistant if she can give you a sample of the shade that you think might be the one, so that you can try it out on your whole face at home and see whether or not it really works for you before you make up your mind.

4 Applying it well

- Give your skin some time to settle when you wake up in the morning before you put any make-up on it.

- Prepare the skin first – think of it as the foundation of the foundation. If you start with a smooth canvas, you will be able to apply your foundation so that it will look invisible. Truly radiant make-up starts with radiant skin. Cleanse, exfoliate, tone and moisturize and let the moisturizer sink in for at least ten minutes.

> Top Tip: A moisturizer that is oil free will work best under foundation as sometimes the oils in moisturizers can react with the oils in foundations, resulting in an uneven finish.

- Brush your teeth and apply lip balm at this stage also, so that it has had plenty of time to settle before you need to apply any lipstick.
- Make sure that you have good light in your bathroom (or wherever you are putting your make-up on) and remember that make-up applied in natural daylight will look good under any lighting conditions.
- Before you start, make sure that your hands are clean. Germs from your hands can transfer and then stay in containers or products, and get transferred onto your face (possibly repeatedly) later on.
- For a more natural, nonchalant look, you may only need to apply foundation where it is necessary. Applying just a dot of foundation to the nose and blending that outwards from the centre is all that some people need to even out the skin tone.
- For a polished look, apply foundation all over. Use a finger, sponge or brush to apply five small dots (see Figure 2.14).

figure 2.14 dot foundation

You can apply stick foundation directly onto the skin, but you get more control by doing it with your finger, sponge or brush. Compact powder is best applied with a sponge or brush, or for a really sheer finish, you can use a fluffy powder brush.

• Then either using fingers, a sponge or a foundation brush, blend outwards with small strokes. Around the eyes pat gently, don't rub. Apply a little more foundation if you think you need to, but remember that the forehead and cheeks don't always need as much. If you have gone right out to the edge of the face, make sure that you don't forget to blend down into your neck. If you have the right shade, it should match completely and blend away easily. The finished foundation should gently fade to nothing around the hairline and jaw line.

Top Tip: If you think you have applied too much, tone it down by dabbing with a clean dry sponge. This works like blotting paper to soak up any excess and shouldn't leave you with the streaks that you would get from trying to wipe it off.

• For the best-looking result, don't try to completely cover a broken out face with a thick layer of foundation. Use a small amount of foundation on the whole face and then use concealer to hide blemishes (see the section on clever concealing, below).

• Any imperfections that are still visible should then be dealt with using concealer (see below) and then the foundation should be set using powder (see the section on perfect powder, page 129).

Clever concealing

Concealers give more coverage than foundations do and are used to camouflage or 're-touch' any facial imperfections. At work, I can save my clients time and money in re-touching and Photoshop costs if I have disguised blemishes well enough that, once they are lit by the photographer, they can't be seen anymore. Once you have read this section, you will know as much about concealing as I do.

Concealers can be used alone without foundation – sometimes this is all you need – or they can be used together with foundation for a really flawless finish – perfect for a special occasion, or if you are going to be photographed. Well-applied concealer can lighten and brighten a face and any blemishes can be hidden from sight. It can also make you appear well rested, even if you're not.

I prefer to apply concealer after foundation for two reasons:

1 Once foundation is applied, sometimes you don't need as much concealer as you might have thought you did.

2 If you apply it first, sometimes you end up wiping it all off again when you apply your foundation over the top.

Just like foundations, many modern concealers are now made to work together with your skin care and they can contain all kinds of active ingredients, including blemish, anti-ageing, and line smoothing treatments. If the aim of make-up is to make you look like yourself, only better, then learning how to use concealer properly is one of the most important things that you can do.

Types of concealer

- *Cream* Cream concealers are usually smooth and creamy to touch. This consistency makes them good for concealing around the delicate eye area because they are not too heavy and drying. They can be applied using a flat concealer brush or your middle finger (better because it applies less pressure than your index finger). If the consistency is really smooth and creamy, these formulas may not be the best for hiding blemishes as well.

- *Stick* Stick concealers usually have a slightly heavier, waxier consistency than cream concealers. This consistency makes them good for concealing imperfections like blemishes, scars and any redness (e.g. broken capillaries or rosacea) because they are more likely to stay put and will often give a bit more coverage than a smoother formulation. This, on the other hand, means that they are not always suitable for use around the delicate eye area. For precise application, the best brush to use is one with a small pointy tip (see section on tools, page 115). They can sometimes be medicated so that they both hide and treat blemishes in one go.

> Top Tip: If you have a stick foundation it can double as a concealer too.

- *Liquid (wand or tube)* Liquid concealers have a light consistency, which, like creams, makes them perfect for using around the delicate eye area. This consistency also makes them good to use if you have sensitive or mid/later stage skin, as it means that there is less product on your skin to either aggravate it or collect in fine lines. The wand style can be applied directly onto the skin, and the tube style can be applied using a flat concealer brush or your middle finger (better because it applies less pressure than your index finger.) This lightweight consistency may not be good for hiding blemishes as well.

- *Pencil* Pencil concealers are often the thickest and most dry and waxy in consistency. This makes them good, and easy to use, for covering blemishes, scars and any redness (e.g. broken capillaries or rosacea). You can literally 'draw' gently onto anything that you want to cover and then all you need to do is make sure that the edges are blended – a cotton bud is best for this (if you try to use your finger, you might just end up wiping it all off again!). Pencils are also often medicated so that they both hide and treat blemishes in one go. If applying directly to spots, make sure to clean or sharpen the pencil directly afterwards to stop it from holding onto any bacteria.

Top Tip: Pencil concealers are great for correcting wobbly lip liner.

- *Corrective* Corrective concealers come in special shades that can be used either alone, or most often blended with another appropriate concealer to 'cancel out' certain other shades. Peach tones are great for cancelling out the blue tones that are often visible in under-eye circles, and yellow tones are great for cancelling out any redness (spots, scars, broken capillaries, rosacea). They can be applied using either your middle finger or a concealer brush (flat or pointy) – whichever is most appropriate. The way that I usually do it is to apply it in layers. A light layer of corrective concealer, applied and blended as normal (see below) should be followed by a light layer of concealer to match into the skin tone or the foundation – apply gently so as not to wipe the first layer off in the process.

- *Light-reflective* Light-reflective concealers contain tiny particles that reflect light, creating luminosity. This makes them great for diffusing the appearance of under-eye shadows by lightening up the whole area. These are most often in a pen style dispenser and can be applied directly onto the skin and then blended with either a flat concealer brush or your middle finger (better because it applies less pressure than your index finger). Avoid using light-reflective concealers on puffy eyes or spots because you may just end up drawing more attention to them.

> Top Tip: Less is more with these concealers, especially if you might be having your picture taken. Flash photography + too many light-reflective particles under your eyes = freaky bright white patches in the photos.

Choose the right shade

- As with foundations, don't test these out on your hands, because hands are very rarely the same colour as faces. Test shades directly on your face and check them outside in the daylight (with a small mirror) just to be sure.
- *For concealing around the eye* The most flattering shade to go for is one that is slightly yellow toned and is one shade lighter than your skin tone or your foundation.
- *For counteracting blueness under the eyes* Use a corrective concealer that has peachy tones to optically cancel the blueness, together with one that is slightly yellow and one shade lighter than your skin tone.
- *For concealing blemishes* The shade needs to match skin tone exactly. Using pale concealer on a blemish can make it look like a white-head.
- *For counteracting redness (blemishes, scars broken capillaries or rosacea)* Use a corrective concealer that is more yellow toned to optically cancel the redness, together with one that matches your skin tone.

How to apply

- A good mirror and good light will make this much quicker and easier. It will be more likely to look better afterwards as well.
- If you haven't already done the foundation step, then make sure that the skin is cleansed, exfoliated, toned and moisturized. Without foundation, it is important to make the skin look as good as possible. Let the moisturizer sink in for ten minutes before applying any concealer.
- If you haven't already done it at the foundation stage, this is a good opportunity to brush your teeth and apply lip balm so that it has time to settle before you might want to apply any lipstick.

- Apply under-eye concealer first, and start by using less concealer than you think that you need. If your under-eye area isn't too bad or if you are just creating a natural look, you can skip this step and go straight to dealing with blemishes.
- Using your finger or flat concealer brush, dot under the eye from next to your nose to about the middle of your eye. If you are using a wand style concealer, you can apply it directly. Don't apply too close to the inner corner of the eye as this can cause the eye to water. If this does happen, hold a cotton bud gently against the outer corner of your eye until it has stopped. If you need to correct any blueness, do this first, in the same way, and blend it before applying any other concealer.

Top Tip: Something that I always do at this stage when I am making people up, is I use the same concealer that I have just used under the eye area, and I dab and blend a tiny bit just next to the outer corner of each eye, and also in the creases of the nose and the outer corners of the mouth. If you have chosen a good under-eye concealer that is slightly yellow toned, this will cancel out any redness and lighten all these areas up. The eyes will look more open and all the features on the face will seem a little bit more perfect.

- Once applied, this needs to be blended so that it looks natural. The point of blending is to not see the edges of the product. If you can't see where it starts or ends then you are less likely to notice it at all. I like to use my middle finger, but you can also do it with your brush, or even a sponge if you like. Use a dabbing or patting motion as opposed to a rubbing or wiping motion. Imagine that you are gently trying to press the concealer into the skin. Rubbing or wiping just removes most of it and then you want to apply more and more because it's not concealing properly, and you can just end up with a big mess.

Top Tip: Avoid having too much product in areas where you have lots of lines, as it will end up collecting there and drawing attention to them as opposed to concealing them. You can end up looking heavily made up and tired – the opposite of what you are trying to do.

- To deal with under-eye bags it is important to realize that rather than covering them up, what you are actually going to do is to draw attention away from them. First make sure that your concealer doesn't contain any light-reflective particles and then apply it only to the darker area under the puffiness. Once blended and set, this can minimize the look of any puffiness under the eyes.
- To deal with blemishes and other imperfections, using a small pointy brush, dab a tiny amount of concealer onto the blemish or other imperfection. If you are using a pencil, you can apply it directly. Try not to be too heavy-handed. You are trying to create an optical illusion with the light, not tippex out a mistake. Most people use far too much concealer when often only the slightest amount is necessary to do the job. Once you have enough concealer, gently blend away the edges using either a cotton bud or wipe any excess off your brush and use that.
- The whole face is now ready to be set with a dusting of powder (see the section on perfect powder, below)
- The final thing is light-reflective concealer. You could apply this before powder, but my personal preference is to apply it afterwards as I find that it tends to stay in place better if the face has already been set with powder. It should be applied slightly underneath where any under-eye concealer was applied, or slightly underneath the area that you are detracting attention from – not directly on top. Don't forget that the secret to this product is that it plays tricks with the light. It is great for brightening the whole face up by bringing more light into the eye area, and making the eyes seem brighter and more open. I actually prefer to apply this at the very end of a make-up, as a finishing touch, after everything else has been done.

Top Tip: A dab of light-reflective concealer at the inner corner of the eye can really brighten the whole face.

Perfect powder

Powder is important for two reasons:

1 it locks your foundation and/or concealer in place, stopping it from sliding off your face
2 it helps to absorb any excess oil and combat any shine that may appear during the day, (although touch-ups may be necessary).

Like foundation, powder also has a bit of a bad reputation. People think that it's going to make their make-up look heavy and theatrical – which it can, of course, but that is purely down to application technique. Modern powders are lightweight and silky smooth, not heavy and chalky. All you need is a delicate dusting and your base is set and your blank canvas is ready to be taken in whichever direction you want to go.

> Top Tip: The darker your skin is naturally, the more shiny it is likely to appear. Try not to go overboard with powder – try using an oil control lotion to help.

Types of powder

- *Loose powder* This comes in a pot or tub and can be matt finish or have shimmer particles for a radiant effect. It can be applied with either a fluffy powder brush or with a powder puff. Best for at-home application – the last thing you want is a pot of loose powder coming open in your handbag!

- *Compact powder* This is also known as pressed powder because it is powder that has been pressed into a compact. Compact powder usually has a matt finish, but can also be available with shimmer particles. Like loose powder it can also be applied with either a fluffy powder brush or with a powder puff. Better than loose powder for on-the-go application or through-the-day touch-ups, but is equally as good at home if you don't want to have two products.

- *Puff applicator* The newest type on the market, these are powder and applicator all in one. They are both easy to use and easy to transport. You apply the powder by simply dabbing the applicator onto your face, then you can also use it to blend away the excess.

- *Blotting sheets* These are special oil-absorbing papers that can lift oil off the surface of the skin without leaving behind any powdery residue. Great for through-the-day touch-ups and a must-have for those with oily skin.

Choose the right shade

Powders are often available in all the same shades that foundations are available in. It is tempting to just buy the one that 'matches'. In my opinion this isn't necessary. A yellow-toned powder can work on pretty much any skin tone, right up to really dark. If you can't find one that is really yellow, then a neutral translucent one with more yellowy than pinky undertones would also suit most skin tones. If you are really tanned, or if you have olive or dark skin you might consider a warmer shade of powder, but beware of shades that are too pinky or orangey.

Powders with shimmer particles can be fantastic for creating a radiant glow, but as with shimmery foundations, you do need to be a little bit careful. Shimmer powder loves to sit in creases and can therefore highlight any lines that might be on the face. They should also be avoided if you have oily skin.

How to apply with a brush

This gives a more sheer, lightweight finish, and is great for barely-there natural make-up looks.

There are many different ways to apply powder using a brush. This is the way that I like to do it:

- Either shake a little loose powder into the lid of your powder pot and then load up your brush with powder that is in the lid, or swirl your brush around a few times in your compact to loosen the powder grains and then load up your brush with that.
- Use the brush to dab this powder all over the face. Don't worry if it seems as though there is too much powder on your face. Don't forget to lightly push the brush into the areas around your nose and to dab your eyelids and ears.
- Shake all the remaining powder out of the brush by tapping the stem of the brush across the back of your hand.
- Then sweep the now empty brush over your whole face, 'dusting off' all the excess powder that you just applied, leaving behind only the sheerest veil of powder to set the foundation in place. This method works really well if you are worried about powder looking dry and cakey. End by sweeping downwards to smooth any downy hairs.
- Look up to the ceiling and sweep the still empty brush under your eyes to make sure that any last traces of powder don't settle into any lines.
- If you are worried about T-zone shine, you can dust another tiny bit of powder across the forehead, nose and chin.

Top Tip: If any blemishes are visible at this stage, use your pointy concealer brush to dab a tiny bit more concealer on them and then set with a cotton bud dipped in a tiny bit of powder.

How to apply with a puff

This leaves much more powder on the face and is good for setting make-up that has to stay on for a long time, or for a look that is a bit more sophisticated or dramatic.

- Either:
  - shake a little loose powder into the lid of your powder pot and dab your puff into the powder that is in the lid
  - or rub the puff gently onto the surface of your pressed powder to lift some off onto the puff
- Dab and press the puff gently onto the face to transfer the powder from the puff. Don't be tempted to rub or wipe with the puff, you will end up messing up the foundation and concealer underneath.
- Continue until the whole face is 'set'.

Top Tip: You can get rid of any excess powder by dabbing gently with a clean part of your puff.

Easy eyebrows

People often underestimate the visual effect that shaping your eyebrows can have. Well-groomed brows frame the face and draw attention to the eyes. They make the eyes look bigger and brighter, they make the nose look thinner and they make the forehead look higher. This mimics the effects of a face-lift; the face looks instantly fresher and more youthful.

There are many ways to remove the stray hairs from your eyebrows and everyone will have their own preference although tweezing, waxing, threading, depilatory creams and electrolysis seem to be the most popular.

Types of eyebrow hair removal

- *Threading (also called fatlah or khite)* This can last four to eight weeks. It is done by moving a piece of tightly twisted cotton across the brow, catching the hairs and removing several at once (see Figure 2.15). It is very quick, isn't as irritating as waxing, but can be a little more painful than tweezing because more hairs are pulled at once. You can get a really clean finish, but it must be done by an experienced therapist.

- *Waxing* This can last four to eight weeks. It is done by painting the hairs that are to be removed with a warm wax and then placing cloth strips over the wax and peeling them away, lifting the hairs with the wax (see Figure 2.16). A good therapist can do this very quickly so it can be relatively pain-free – stragglers can be tweezed, but waxing can get most of the fine hairs too. It is quick and clean (if done well), but you have less control over the shape and some people find it painful.

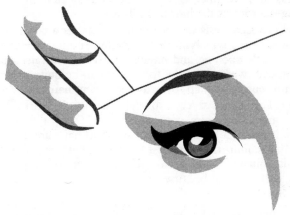

figure 2.15 threading

figure 2.16 waxing

- *Depilatory creams* These can last several days to two weeks. Depilatory creams work by dissolving the visible parts of the hairs that they are applied to so that they can be washed or wiped away. They work quickly and are inexpensive to buy and easily available, but be sure to buy a special 'face' formulation. They can however be a bit messy, and some people are put off by the smell. Depilatory creams are not recommended for use by people with sensitive skin, and re-growth is not as fine as other methods which involve removing the root of the hair as well.

- *Electrolysis* Electrolysis can be permanent (after a course of sessions). It works by having a thin sterile wire inserted into the hair follicle opening and having an electric current sent down the wire which kills the follicle. It can be quite pricey and painful but it is a step towards permanent hair removal.

- *Tweezing* This can last two to eight weeks. It works by plucking unwanted hairs out one by one using a pair of tweezers. It can be a bit tricky on really short hairs and it can be slightly uncomfortable the first few times, but you get used to it quite quickly. This is my personal favourite type of eyebrow hair removal because I feel like once you get into a routine, the upkeep is simple and speedy.

If you have never shaped your eyebrows before and you are scared that it all might end in disaster, go to a professional for your first time, and then use their shape as a template for easy upkeep afterwards (if you do it once a week you should never lose the shape). Or use my guide to try it yourself at home.

Step-by-step guide to perfect eyebrows

Step 1: a good pair of tweezers

For the ultimate in ease and precision a quite sharp, slant-edged pair of tweezers is the best. The sharpness means that the tweezers have more grip which means that they will remove even the most obstinate of hairs and the whole process is much quicker and easier. Keep your tweezers clean and sterile by either running them under a hot tap, or dipping into alcohol or surgical spirit before and after each use.

Step 2: position

Try to use a good mirror with good light. It can be difficult to pluck your brows looking into a small hand mirror as your scope of vision is very restricted and a small mirror can only reflect so much light. Using a large vertical mirror flooded with light will make a big difference not only to how much you can see, but to how well you can see it. Natural light, i.e. by a window, is the best.

Top Tip: Shavata, the Eyebrow Expert, suggests using two mirrors when shaping your brows. She says 'Use a hand mirror for close-up plucking and a large mirror to step back and look at both brows as you pluck, checking that the brows are even.'

Step 3: timing

The optimum time to tweeze is directly after a bath or a shower. The skin is more supple and it is much easier to remove the hairs. Alternatively, a warm flannel held over the face for 30 seconds will help to open the pores in the same way.

Top Tip: Avoid tweezing in the run-up to and week of your period as it is much more painful then because the skin is more sensitive.

Step 4: guide

If you are nervous about plucking, you can use a white eye-pencil to draw on your brow marking the area that needs to be plucked (see Figure 2.17).

Follow the shape guide in Step 5. Wipe any excess pencil away afterwards.

Step 5: shape

For a natural-looking 'groomed' brow, follow the natural curve of the top edge of your brow and tweeze only from underneath and between the brows.

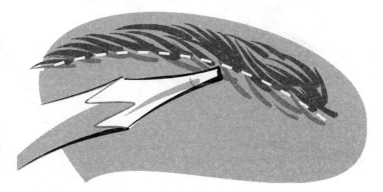

figure 2.17 tweezing guide

Top Tip: Shavata, the Eyebrow Expert, advises to 'never pluck above the brow' because 'this is your natural shape' and 'it will never grow back the same'.

The ideal shape can be plotted along three points and is a representation of the golden ratio (see Figure 2.18). The Golden Ratio is a mathematical theory, and shapes that follow the golden ratio are generally accepted as being aesthetically pleasing.

The start point (A) The brow should start at a point vertically above the centre of your nostril – you can find this point by holding a pencil or brush vertically against your nose.

The highest point (B) The highest point should be directly above the outer edge of your iris; the coloured part of your eye.

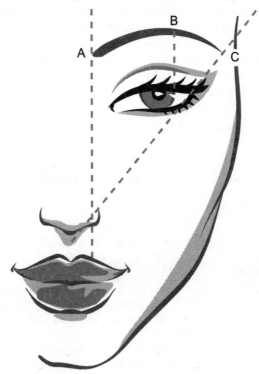

figure 2.18 eyebrow shape

The end point (C) To find where the brow should end, hold your brush or pencil diagonally joining your nostril and the corner of your eye. The brow should end where it meets the brush/pencil.

Step 6: tweezing

• Pull the skin taut with the opposite hand – this not only reduces the sting, makes it easier to see the line of the brow.

• Place the tweezers close to the skin, near the roots of the hair and pluck one hair at a time with a quick motion in the direction of the hair growth.

> Top Tip: The quicker you pull, the less it will hurt.

• Alternate frequently between brows to ensure symmetry.

• Make sure you stop regularly to stand back and check from a distance – this helps to stop you from getting carried away and over-tweezing.

• Resist the urge to over-tweeze – just tidying up a few stray hairs can quickly make a huge difference.

> Top Tip: If your brow needs soothing afterwards, dab it with an ice cube wrapped in a flannel.

• Keeping your tweezers clean and sterile by wiping them with either some alcohol or disinfectant after each use (and preferably before) reduces any chance of infection.

Step 7: filling in

This isn't always necessary, but it can give a more polished finish, and is also handy for correcting any mistakes as a result of overzealous tweezing.

Types of eyebrow products

• *Pencil* You can fill in using an eyebrow pencil – these are usually a bit harder than a kohl or eyeliner pencil. This is so that they are less likely to smudge and you can be more precise in your application.

• *Powder* Alternatively you can use eyebrow powder, which is basically eye-shadow with a slightly waxier texture. Eye-shadow will work fine if you don't use too much powder at a time and work slowly and build up in layers. It can be easier to create a softer look with powder, but you need to watch out for stray bits of powder falling everywhere.

Getting the right shade

Don't immediately go for a colour that is too dark. When you fill in your brows with either pencil or powder, it doesn't necessarily have to match your hair colour. It only needs to create a shadow. For a natural look most people can get away with a blonde pencil. I would only use a darker shade if you want really defined brows for a specific make-up look, or for if you are correcting a tweezing blunder.

How to apply

Pencil

- Unless you are going for a really 'pencilled-in' look, avoid drawing in one stroke right across the brow, instead try using feathery short strokes as if you are drawing hairs in the gaps.

Top Tip: Some people like to use a really sharp pencil for this, I actually quite like my pencil to have a slightly softened tip, so I often soften it on my hand before I start.

- Blend and brush into shape with an eyebrow brush, an old, clean, mascara wand, or even a toothbrush. Use upward and outward strokes.

Powder

- Load up a stiff, angled brush with a small amount of powder.

Top Tip: Avoid stray bits of powder falling everywhere by tapping the stem of the brush across the back of your hand to remove any excess powder.

- Then apply to the brows using soft short strokes as if you are filling in the gaps between the hairs.
- Blend and brush into shape with an eyebrow brush or even a toothbrush (baby ones are great for this). Use upward and outward strokes.
- Don't panic if you overdo it or make a mistake as this is easily fixed with a cotton bud dipped in a little bit of eye make-up remover.
- Then, when you are satisfied with your work, set it in place using either a special eyebrow gel, or a brow grooming brush sprayed with hairspray. Apply by brushing the hairs upwards and outwards.

How to highlight

Highlighters are fantastic make-up tools because you can use them to play clever tricks with the light which can suggest radiant complexions and defined cheekbones that aren't actually there! Anywhere that you apply highlighter on your face will pick up more light, and reflect it back quicker than un-highlighted areas, giving the illusion that the highlighted areas are drawn forward slightly, or are higher.

Highlighting the cheekbones can not only make you look fresher, younger and healthier, but it gives blusher a more three-dimensional feel, making it look more natural and less like make-up. You can also bring more light into the eyes to create a bit of added sparkle or highlight the lips for a more plumped-up pout. A flawless flat base can suddenly come alive and seem more real when you add in some highlights.

If you have oily or problem skin, be really careful how you apply highlighter, and keep it to a minimum – eyes and lips are ok, cheeks might be a problem. If you have later stage skin, you need to be careful about highlighter settling in lines, but it works great on the cheeks to add a healthy, youthful glow.

Types of highlighter

- *Cream* These are usually a smooth and creamy texture, and I find that they work best when applied using my fingers. Because the texture mimics that of the skin, they are good for a natural looking finish. They are easier to control than liquids or powders and are best applied before face powder.

- *Stick* Stick highlighters have the same consistency as creams, but you can apply them directly onto the skin. This can be quick, but you have less control over how much product gets onto the skin. Less is more with highlighters (as it is with most things) and, again, it is easiest to use your fingers to apply and build up as necessary.

- *Liquid* Liquid highlighters have a consistency that is similar to liquid foundation. They can be tricky to apply if you are trying to highlight a specific area – I find creams a bit easier to blend into foundation. They are, however, very easy to use over your whole face, say as a radiance booster, either alone or underneath a satin or matt finish foundation.

Top Tip: Liquid highlighters are great for mixing in with other products (e.g. matt or satin finish foundation, liquid or gel blush or even body lotion) to transform them and add a subtle shimmer.

- *Powder* Powder highlighters come in various forms. They can look like shimmery compact powders, shimmery blushers, pots of shimmer dust and tubs of shiny beads. You can even double up an ivory, gold or peachy coloured shimmer eye-shadow as a shimmer powder. They are best applied with a brush as you may end up with far too much on your face if you use your fingers or a sponge. Remember that powder collects in creases and shimmer highlights, so avoid highlighter powders if your skin is later stage and stick with creams or liquids.

> Top Tip: A dust of highlighter powder is a great way to dress up an otherwise naked *décolleté*.

- *Powder/applicator all-in-one* These are powder highlighters that have either a brush or a puff attached. They are absolutely fantastic for dusting across the *décolleté* (as mentioned above), but be wary of using them on the face because you have less control over how much is actually dispensed.
- *Pencil* Pencil highlighters are often quite chunky and are brilliant for highlighting small areas like under the eyebrow and the inner corner of the eye.

Getting the shade right

- *for pale complexions* ivory, pink, peach or even lavender tones work well
- *for olive or tanned complexions* peach or gold tones work well
- *for darker complexions* gold or bronze tones work well.

> Top Tip: Tone down highlighter that is too shimmery mixing it with a bit of foundation.

How to apply

- Remember that less is more, and that it is always much easier to add more than it is to take away. So start by just using a little and build up as necessary to create the effect that you want.
- Blending is key with highlighter. If done well, it can create the illusion of radiant skin, higher cheekbones and brighter eyes. Done badly and you just look like you have stripes of shiny stuff on your face.

- Keep all highlighter products away from the centre of your T-zone (i.e. the centre of your forehead and your nose). This area is prone to being shiny, so we don't need to make it even more difficult for ourselves by adding extra shine!
- Be careful with any bumps and lines, as too much highlighter can end up drawing more attention to them.
- Don't overdo it. Highlighter only works if it has something to be highlighted against. If you have got highlighter everywhere, nothing can stand out any more and it defeats the purpose.

Top Tip: The easiest way to apply highlighter is to just dab a tiny bit on top of your blusher, right in the middle of the apples of the cheeks – it softens the blusher and makes it look more natural.

To highlight cheekbones using a cream highlighter:

- Do this before bronzer and blusher.
- Using your middle finger, apply dots of highlighter in a 'C' shape around each eye, following the line of the cheekbone up and around the temple. Begin below and end above the middle of your eye (see Figure 2.19).

figure 2.19 highlighter 'C' shape

- By reflecting more light, this gives the illusion that the cheek bones and brow bones are slightly higher than they actually are, which defines the shape of the face more. At the same time, it draws more light around the eye area, which automatically makes people focus more on the eyes when they look at you.

To highlight cheekbones using a powder highlighter:

- Do this after bronzer and blusher.
- Remove any traces of blusher from your blusher brush by wiping it on a tissue.
- Dab the brush into your highlighter powder (if it is a pot, shake a tiny bit out first and dab your brush into that).

> Top Tip: Make sure that there isn't too much on the brush by tapping the stem of the brush across the back of your hand to remove any excess powder.

- Stroke the highlighter along the top of each cheekbone and then do a dab just above each brow.
- Wipe the brush off to get rid of any remaining highlighter.
- Blend away the edges with your now clean brush.

To bring out eyes:

- This brings more light into the inner corner of the eye. It makes eyes look like they are fresher, more open and wide-awake. It is especially good if you have deep or small-set eyes.
- Dot any sort of highlighter (except for the all-in-one applicator type which might be a bit too big!) in the inner corner of the upper eye-lids (see Figure 2.20). It brightens the whole eye area and makes eyes look wide open and beautiful in the light. Be careful with powder – don't let it fall into, and highlight, any fine lines under the eyes.

> Top Tip: If you have dry and flaky or wrinkly eyelids, replace the highlighter with a pale concealer. It will have a similar effect of drawing more light into the area, without the downside of the shimmer highlighting all the flakes and lines.

- Finish off with a tiny dab blended just underneath the eyebrow, which then opens the eye up from the other side as well.

figure 2.20 highlight inner corner of eye

To accent the lips:

- A dab of highlighter applied to the cupid's bow (the dip in the centre of your upper lip line), can give the illusion of a fuller top lip. Pencil highlighters work really well for this.
- A dab of highlighter applied to the centre of the lower lip can give the illusion of a fuller lower lip. I find cream highlighters work best for this.
- For a really full pout, do both!

Top Tip: You can make your own shimmery lip-gloss by mixing a tiny bit of highlighter powder with clear gloss on the back of your hand. Mix it well and apply just to the centre of your mouth with a lip brush or a fingertip. If you want to use lip balm instead of gloss, then mix that with a tiny bit of cream highlighter.

Better bronzer

I love bronzers, and I rarely do a make-up on someone without using some bronzer somewhere. It might be to create a bit of definition, but more than likely it will be to warm the complexion and inject a natural-looking healthy radiance. The quickest and easiest way to recreate that 'just got back from holiday' look, is with a delicate dusting of bronzer, which makes it a great instant winter cheer-up!

It's not just for your face, though. Bronzed legs look longer and slimmer and a dusting of bronzer can add the finishing touches to a party frock by giving you sexy shoulders and a more contoured cleavage.

Types of bronzer

• *Powder* Powder bronzers can be in loose or compact form. The compact ones are easy to apply and work best with a big fluffy brush like a blusher brush or even a powder brush. They can be used all over the face and body to give an all-over bronze glow. They can also be used to shade and contour the face, although matt powders or only slightly shimmery ones work better for this. Loose ones work the same way, you just need to be careful about not overloading your brush. The best way to be sure is to tip a tiny bit into the lid and then dip your brush into that.

Top Tip: Powder bronzer can easily double as eyeshadow.

• *Cream* Cream bronzers usually have a smooth and creamy texture that makes them easy to blend into the skin or foundation. They are best applied with fingers and can also be used to create an all-over glow, or more specific definition. As with powders, though, avoid using anything too sparkly for shading – it defeats the purpose. Their texture means that they can look more natural on the skin, which makes them great for creating fresh and natural make-up looks, and also for using on dry or later stage skins.

Top Tip: Mix a bit of shimmery cream bronzer with your regular body lotion to give a subtle sun-kissed glow to your whole body.

• *Stick* Stick bronzers have the same texture and effect as cream bronzers and are often sold as multi-function products that can be used on lips, eyes and body too. They can be applied directly onto the skin, but if you are at all worried about applying too much, use your fingers so that you have more control.

• *Liquid/gel* Liquid and gel bronzers can be the most tricky to apply, but their texture makes them look the most natural on the skin. Sometimes they come with applicators, sometimes not. If not, then a make-up sponge or cotton wool pad should make it a little easier for you. Wash your hands afterwards – you might have bronzed fingertips too!

Top Tip: I often use liquid bronzers at work on models' legs instead of fake tan, because it's quick, easy, you don't have to wait for it to develop and you can wash it off at the end of the day. The ones with a bit of shimmer in work the best.

- *Powder/applicator all-in-one* These powder bronzers are usually shimmery and have either a puff or brush applicator attached and can be great for dusting the décolleté or quick touch-ups through the day. Have a good practice before you use them, though, because you have less control over how much powder is dispensed and it could be very easy to overdo it by mistake.

Getting the shade right

- As a general rule, avoid anything that is too sparkly or has too much orange in it – the aim of bronzer is to look sun-kissed, not tangoed!
- Remember that bronzers that have too much shimmer in them work to shade and highlight all at the same time. So you might be happily trying to define your cheekbones using your bronzer without realizing that the highlighter in it might actually be making them look rounder.

Top Tip: A good all-round bronzer that suits pretty much everyone is a matt light brown with a hint of shimmer through it.

- If you have oily or later stage skin and are at all worried about shimmer, then stick with a matt one – you can always layer a tiny bit of shimmer highlighter over the top if you want to.
- If you have pale skin, choose the palest bronzer that you can find.
- The darker your skin tone, the darker you can go with your bronzer. But, as a general rule, using a bronzer that is darker than the colour of the skin on your chest is not going to look as natural.

How to apply

- To create a natural, healthy-looking, glistening glow, you need to apply a little bit of bronzer to all the areas where the sun would natural hit your face. If you apply it all over your face it can be too heavy.

- As with everything, remember that less is more and that its much easier to add a little more than it is to take away – this involves wiping and can lead to streaks.
- Blending is very important. If you walk around with unblended bronzer you might get people trying to wipe a 'dirty mark' off your face.
  - *Powder* Dust gently over forehead, around temples, under cheekbones and down neck.
  - *Cream, stick, liquid* Dab and blend a small amount in the centre of the forehead, on the temples, under the cheekbones and a little on the neck (see Figure 2.21).

> Top Tip: For a really natural finish, sweep a little over the eyelids and in the hairline as well.

- For sculpted cheekbones, apply and blend a couple of layers of a matt bronzer underneath the cheekbone, following its line all the way up to the hairline (see Figure 2.22). For extra effect dab a touch of highlighter (see the section on how to highlight, page 139) along the top of the cheekbone.

figure 2.21 dot bronzing cream

figure 2.22 sculpt cheekbones

Top Tip: A simple way to complement your new creamy caramel complexion is to add a swirl of shimmery blusher on the apples of the cheeks and a slick of gloss on the mouth, to catch the light and give a subtle sun-kissed finish.

- Dust or dab over shoulders and *décolleté* for glowing skin and remember that a touch of bronzer in the cleavage can give an extra boost of definition.

Beautiful blusher

If I were only allowed to have one make-up product it would be blusher. I love blusher. For me it is the ultimate make-up quick fix. It works in a flash to transform and add life and vitality to every face. If I feel a bit rubbish in the morning, sometimes I just put on a dab of bright blusher (nothing else) and my face looks instantly healthier and more awake. I like the person looking back at me in the mirror much better than the washed-out one without the blusher and I feel immediately much better about myself. That is the magic of blusher!

Blushers come in a whole array of colours and textures that can be dabbed, dusted or blended to suit any skin tone or type to create any sort of look. Blusher can be worn on its own for a subtle flush or layered together with bronzer and highlighter for perfectly sculpted features. I know that lots of people use their bronzers as blushers, and there is nothing wrong with that at all. But if you can get into the idea of using blusher together with bronzer, it can open a up a whole new world of possibilities with your make-up. Just like bronzer, you can also use blusher to warm the skin and contour the cheekbones, but blusher can add that extra bit of flush to the cheeks that you don't get from bronzer on its own. It mimics the flush that we get when we fall in love, and that is the time when we feel and look our most beautiful.

Types of blusher

- *Powder* Powder blush tends to be the simplest to use and is best applied after the face has been powdered with a large blusher brush. If combining with bronzer, I usually do it afterwards because it is really easy to see exactly where you need to put the colour. You can achieve a sheer finish with just a light dusting, or build up to a really strong contoured look by adding lots of layers (think 1980s). Powder blush works well on oily skins, whereas very dry or later stage skins should be wary of too many powdery products on the face drawing attention to flakes and lines. Powder blush has pretty good staying power.

- *Cream* Cream blushers usually have a smooth creamy texture and I think they are best applied with the fingertips using a tapping or dabbing motion to gently press the product on to your cheeks, which you keep doing until the cream is blended away with no harsh edges. Don't be tempted to rub it into your skin, as you will just end up wiping it off. If you are using cream blush for the first time, practise getting used to this dabbing and blending technique before you actually do your make-up. Alternatively, you could use a brush – something like a foundation brush would work quite well, but I prefer fingers. I usually apply cream blush after foundation (or directly onto skin) but before powder, because it is easier to blend and then the powder sets it. As with powder blusher, the intensity of colour depends on how you apply it. If you just apply a tiny bit and blend it well, you will have a subtle flush. If you dab on a few layers, the look will be more dramatic. Creams mimic the texture of the skin so that they can look more natural, and work really well on dry or later stage skin, but they don't tend to last as long as powders.

Top Tip: A rose or tawny toned cream blush can be a brilliant multi-function product that can work on cheeks, lips and eyes!

- *Stick* Stick blushers have the same texture and effect as cream blushers but can be applied directly onto the skin. If you are worried about applying too much, dab it on with your finger – that way you have more control.
- *Mousse* Mousse blushers are very similar to creams except that they are usually a bit more lightweight and have a more matt velvety finish on the skin. Like cream blushers they are best applied with the fingertips using the dabbing and blending technique described above. They are perfect for creating a really subtle flush, which makes them great for later stage skins or for creating looks that are really natural. As with creams and liquids, they are easier to blend, either on bare skin or on foundation before it has been powdered.
- *Liquid* Liquid blushers work really well on bare skin, and if you are wearing foundation, like cream formulas, they are easier to blend before you have applied your powder. They are also fab on any skin stage to just give a translucent rosiness and can double as lip colour.
- *Gel* Like liquid blushers, these work really well on bare skin, or if you are wearing foundation they are easier to blend before you have applied your powder. They are also fab on any skin stage to just give a translucent rosiness and can double as lip colour. They are often a little more translucent or glossy than a cream or a liquid.
- *Stain* These can be the trickiest to apply because they work by staining the skin and can dry quite quickly, so you have to blend them in quite fast. They are fab on any skin stage to just give a translucent rosiness and on bare skin they can last all day long. They can also be great for staining the lips.
- *Puff applicator* These powder blushers usually have a touch of shimmer and are applied by dabbing the applicator directly onto the face. They are handy for transporting and easy to use. You can even use the applicator to blend in any excess if you have applied too much.

Getting the shade right

- To get the most natural-looking blush, you need to use a blusher that matches the colour that your cheeks go after you have exercised – or the colour of your actual blush!
- Personally, I am a big fan of pink blusher and I tend to use pinks more than any other in my kit because I think that, in the right tone, they can flatter everyone.
- Shades with gold and peach tones can also flatter every complexion and are great for creating warm summery looks.
- Basically, the paler your skin tone the more white there needs to be in your blusher to make it complement your skin tone. Avoid using pale-toned blushers if you have dark skin as they can end up looking ashy.

This list breaks down the different types of pink, peach and neutral tones that I think work best on different skin tones:

Fair skin Dusty rose or pale pastel pink, milky peach/apricot, or subtle beige/tawny neutrals.

Olive/yellow-toned skin Rosy or bright pink, warm peach, earthy terracotta/coppery neutrals

Bronze/tanned skin Coral pink, warm orange or red, warm bronze/berry neutrals

Dark/black skin Deep plum, bright red, deep berry/cocoa neutrals.

- The darker your skin tone, the more intensity you can get away with and still look natural. Obviously, a more intense blush applied to fair skins will create a more dramatic look if so desired, but keep it sheer and translucent for more simple basic looks.
- Shimmery blushers can be flattering for mid/later skin as they diffuse fine lines, making the delicate skin around your cheeks look younger, but they need to be applied sparingly so as not to collect in the lines and end up highlighting them instead of diffusing them. Creamier textures are a good option.

How to apply

- To ensure that you never overdo your blush, always apply it before you do your eyes or lips. Treat it as though it were part of your foundation rather than a finishing touch, that way it will always be natural looking.

PLATE 1 basic face

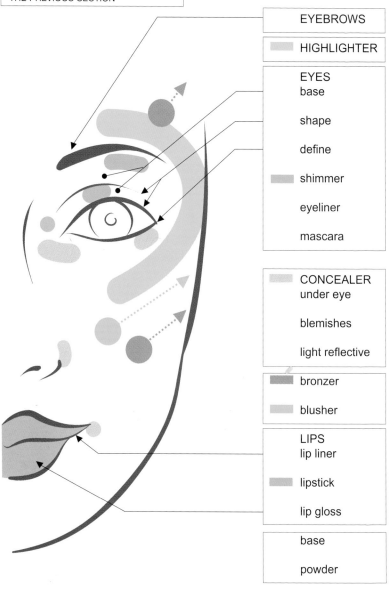

KEY:
COLOURS INDICATE WHERE TO APPLY
DOTTED ARROWS INDICATE DIRECTION
 OF BLENDING
APPLY IN APPROPRIATE ORDER AS IN
 THE PREVIOUS SECTION

EYEBROWS

HIGHLIGHTER

EYES
base

shape

define

shimmer

eyeliner

mascara

CONCEALER
under eye

blemishes

light reflective

bronzer

blusher

LIPS
lip liner

lipstick

lip gloss

base

powder

PLATE 2 basic face chart
(fill in your own product types)

PLATE 3 bride

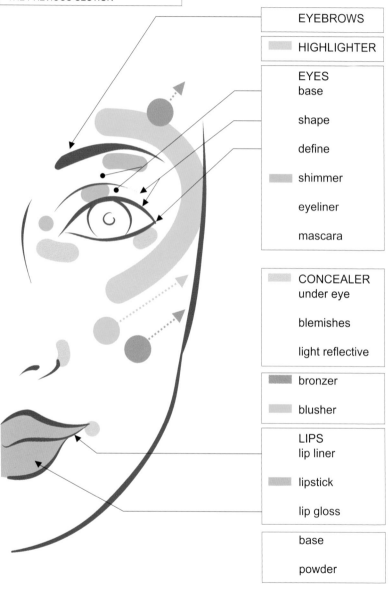

KEY:
COLOURS INDICATE WHERE TO APPLY
DOTTED ARROWS INDICATE DIRECTION
  OF BLENDING
APPLY IN APPROPRIATE ORDER AS IN
  THE PREVIOUS SECTION

EYEBROWS

HIGHLIGHTER

EYES
base

shape

define

shimmer

eyeliner

mascara

CONCEALER
under eye

blemishes

light reflective

bronzer

blusher

LIPS
lip liner

lipstick

lip gloss

base

powder

PLATE 4 bride chart
(fill in your own product types)

PLATE 5 movie star

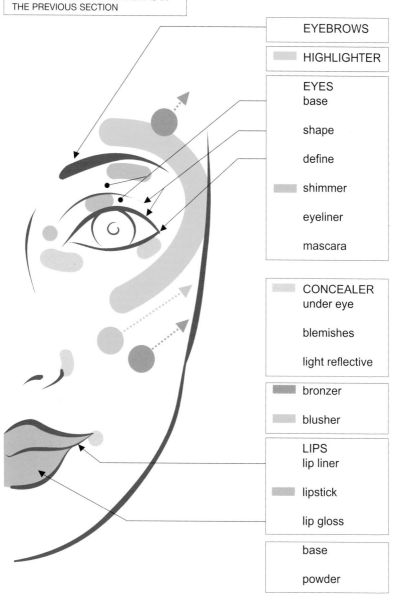

KEY:
COLOURS INDICATE WHERE TO APPLY
DOTTED ARROWS INDICATE DIRECTION
 OF BLENDING
APPLY IN APPROPRIATE ORDER AS IN
 THE PREVIOUS SECTION

EYEBROWS

HIGHLIGHTER

EYES
base

shape

define

shimmer

eyeliner

mascara

CONCEALER
under eye

blemishes

light reflective

bronzer

blusher

LIPS
lip liner

lipstick

lip gloss

base

powder

PLATE 6 movie star chart
(fill in your own product types)

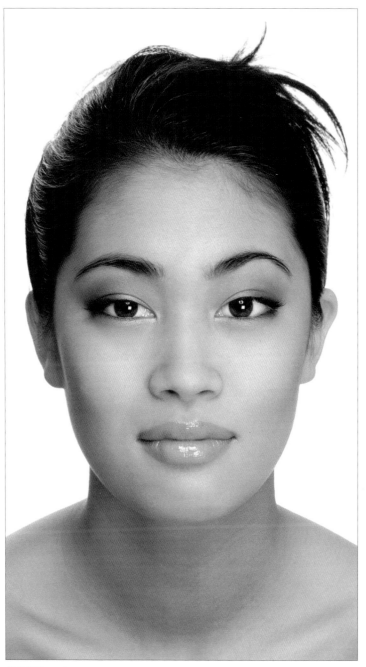

PLATE 7 smoky eye

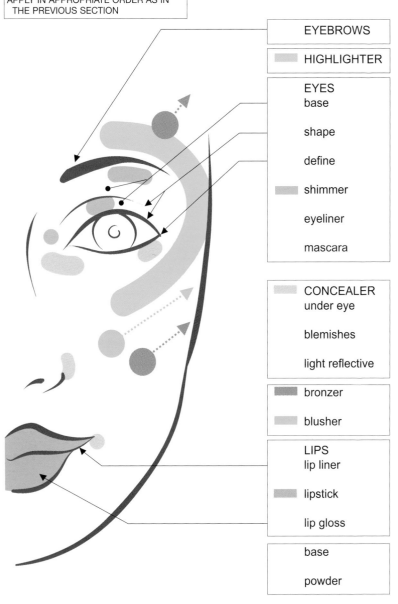

KEY:
COLOURS INDICATE WHERE TO APPLY
DOTTED ARROWS INDICATE DIRECTION
  OF BLENDING
APPLY IN APPROPRIATE ORDER AS IN
  THE PREVIOUS SECTION

EYEBROWS

HIGHLIGHTER

EYES
base

shape

define

shimmer

eyeliner

mascara

CONCEALER
under eye

blemishes

light reflective

bronzer

blusher

LIPS
lip liner

lipstick

lip gloss

base

powder

PLATE 8 smoky eye chart
(fill in your own product types)

- Another way to ensure that you don't apply too much is to make sure that you are doing your make-up in a good mirror with good light (see tools).

151
icing the cake: refining your
beautiful face and body
02

> Top Tip: Be aware that the hue of your blusher can become more intense if your own body temperature rises, so apply it extra-sparingly if you are going anywhere where you are likely to get warm.

- If you are using a powder blusher, a good brush is really important. The tiny ones that come with the compacts are just about OK for through-the-day touch-ups, but for a really good, natural-looking application, a good brush can make all the difference.
- After dipping your brush into the powder, shake off any excess by tapping the stem of the brush on your hand. This prevents you from applying too much at once.
- For a simple, natural-looking, rosy glow, smile and lightly apply blush on the apples of the cheeks (the part that pops up because you are smiling), blending upwards and outwards. For both finger application and brush application, think more along the lines of dabbing and pressing in short feathery strokes to move the colour around as opposed to rubbing and wiping.
- The blush should blend to nothing around the ear/hairline and also approximately two fingers distance away from the edge of your nose, with the concentration of colour on apple of the cheek. When blending outwards towards the hairline, ensure that you avoid the 'Aunt Sally' effect.
- If you apply slightly higher and have the concentration of colour higher up on the cheekbones, the result will be a more sophisticated, less natural look.

> Top Tip: To be absolutely sure that a brush application is perfectly blended, wipe any excess blusher off your brush and then gently sweep it over the cheeks around the edges of the colour. This will soften any harsh lines and make the blusher look more natural.

- A blended dab on the temples, earlobes and chin can help to make blusher look like it naturally belongs on the face, especially if you are not layering it with bronzer.
- If you want to be really sure that your blusher stays put, dust over the top lightly with some face powder.

> Top Tip: For real staying power, apply a layer of powder blush over the top of cream, mousse or liquid blush.

- The ultimate sculpted cheek consists of three layers applied in whatever order is appropriate for the type of product that you are using, e.g. creams before powder. If all three were cream, I would apply highlighter first, then bronzer, and lastly blusher. If all three were powder, I would apply bronzer first, then blusher and lastly highlighter. The bronzer and highlighter redefine the cheekbone and the blusher adds the flush of colour that makes it look more three-dimensional.

- For extra tips and tricks with blusher please refer to the section on professional tips and tricks (page 187).

> Top Tip: For fixing blusher that has gone overboard, try dabbing it gently with a clean dry make-up sponge. This will often be enough to lift off any excess blusher (apart from liquid stains). Failing that, if there is still too much cream/mousse blusher, try blending in a tiny dab of moisturizer or foundation. This should tone down the intensity of colour without ruining the finish. If there is still too much powder blusher, dusting with a generous amount of face powder (and then getting rid of any excess), will also soften colour that is too intense, but be wary of this trick if you have dry or later stage skin.

Shadow secrets

Even though there are what seems like millions of different shades and types of eye shadow out there to choose from, the basic reason to use them remains the same. We want to define and brighten the most expressive feature on our faces: our eyes. Bigger and brighter eyes not only look more youthful (the Bambi effect), they also detract from any other issues that you might want people to pay less attention to (e.g. ageing skin, spots or blemishes.) Eye shadows can give us the key to unlocking the secret potential of our own eyes. By using simple techniques and clever use of colour, we can contrast, highlight and define our way to eyes that are more attractive to look at and therefore more beautiful.

It doesn't have to be scary or complicated. Whether you are a complete eye make-up virgin, or if you are stuck in a bit of a rut and are looking for something new, follow my simple guide and the secrets of eye shadow shall be yours. If you start out by keeping things simple and build up your confidence, you will soon be able to experiment and express yourself in all sorts of ways that you may have never thought possible.

Types of eye product

- *Powder eye shadow* Powder eye shadows are easy to use and can be applied using foam applicator pads, fingers or brushes. Applicator pads and fingers are great for adding a quick wash of colour. Brushes are better for creating definition. Pads and fingers are easy, speedy and you get much more colour 'pay off' from one application, especially from shadows containing shimmer, and you are less likely to make a mess. Brushes can take a bit more practice and if you aren't careful you can end up with eye shadow powder falling onto your face. But you can build up in layers to create stunning results, so a bit of patience and practice can be well worth it.

> Top Tip: For extra staying power, apply powder eye shadow with a damp brush. This can be over the whole lid, or using a flat slanted brush as eyeliner.

- *Cream/mousse eye shadow* Cream or mousse shadows can come in many forms. They can come in pots, in tubes and in stick/pen form, but their textures are generally the same. They are usually lightweight, creamy and very easy to apply and blend. You can apply creams using fingers or brushes, I tend to use my fingers for a quick 'wash' of colour and brushes for something that is more precise and defined. Use a tapping or dabbing motion to gently press the product on to your eyelid until the cream is blended away with no harsh edges. The middle finger works really well for this. Obviously, sticks and pens can be applied directly to the eye, but are blended more easily using fingers or a brush. On their own, creams and mousses can give a much more subtle effect than powder and are great for giving just a subtle wash of colour. Sometimes I layer creams under powders for a much more intense effect. Creams are great for later stage skin.

> Top Tip: Neutral cream eye shadows (ivory, peach, pink and gold shades) can easily double as cream highlighter.

- *Eye gloss* Eye glosses give a glisten to the eye that can be both modern and dramatic. Some have a texture similar to eye creams and others can be more like lip gloss. They are easy to apply using fingers or a brush and can add a subtle wash of colour over the whole eye, or a hint of highlight in the centre of the lid. They can however tend to have a life of their own and can crease, smudge and move around quite easily, and something that started off as sexy and smouldering when you applied it, could end up looking more like the morning after quite quickly.

- *Chunky pencils* Chunky pencils look like really fat eyeliner pencils. Their texture is a bit thicker and waxier than creams, their colour is usually more intense and they have more staying power. I love them because they are so quick and easy to use. If I only have minutes to transform someone from a day look to a night look, I will reach straight for a dark chunky pencil and a blending brush (as explained in the 'smoky eye' section of 'step-by-step make-up looks', page 182).

- *Eyeliner pencils* Like chunky pencils, eyeliner pencils are great tools for quick and easy eye definition. Feathery strokes drawn in at the lash line and then blended with a cotton bud create a subtle soft smoky line around the eyes that makes the eyelashes look longer and the eyes seem more open. This works either alone for simple definition or in combination with either creams or powders for a more polished look. Eyeliner pencils can also be a way to experiment with bolder colours. If you like the idea of trying something bright but the idea of wearing it over your whole eyelid is scary, then try it as eyeliner for just a hint of colour.

- *Liquid/pen eyeliner* Like pencil eyeliner, liquid and pen eyeliner also create the illusion that the eyelashes are longer making the eyes look bigger, but they create a more precise and dramatic line as opposed to a smoky one. They can be a little more tricky to use. Tips for eyeliner application can be found both in the 'movie star' section of 'step-by-step make-up looks' (page 177), and in the section on professional tips and tricks (page 187).

- *Gel eyeliner* Gel eyeliners create the same effect as liquid or pen eyeliners, but they are best applied using a flat slanted brush.

Getting the shade right

- With all the choice that is available, this can be quite an overwhelming task, and sometimes the colours that we like, or are drawn to in the shop, are not the colours that will necessarily flatter our own skin tone and eye colour. Then, as well as getting the shade right, you have to decide whether a matt or shimmer finish will work better with the 'look' that you might want to create.

- For basic eye definition you can't go wrong with matt neutrals: bone, taupe, brown. These tones will work on everyone apart from really dark skins in which case shades like taupe, coffee and cocoa might be a better starting point. To these three basic colours I would also add a shimmery highlighter in a similar tone to the palest of your eye shadows, in this case something like a shimmery ivory. From these basics you can then customize how you apply them by adding in other shades to suit your mood or desired look.

- To add life and sparkle, colours can be used around the eyes to complement and enhance them. For just a hint of colour, a sheer wash of a shimmery gold or bronze can brighten most eyes in a very subtle way – great for natural or barely there looks. Or for a more modern twist, use a brighter colour. To create a bit of drama, smudge a vivid shadow colour on the outer corners of your eye.

- Something soft and shimmery around the eye can really wake up the face if you feel and look tired.

- Apart from the basic neutral palette described above, these are my top picks for colours that work well with certain eye colours. These aren't rules, they are merely recommendations – think of them as a starting point. Try them out, see what you think and then go in your own direction

  - *Brown eyes*
    - Base colours: sand, bronze, pink and khaki
    - Accent colours: rust, charcoal and black
    - Highlight colours: champagne, gold and pink
    - Colour washes: gold, bronze, lilac and pistachio green.

> Top Tip: For an alternative to brown or black to line or accent, try purple. It looks great with brown eyes, especially if you have olive or dark skin.

- *Green/hazel eyes*
  - Base colours: champagne, apricot and khaki
  - Accent colours: brown, forest green and plum
  - Highlight colours: champagne and gold
  - Colour washes: champagne, gold, pale green and rose.

> Top Tip: Bronze eyeliner reflects the gold flecks in green and hazel eyes making it a really flattering way to dress up an otherwise natural look.

- *Blue eyes*
  - Base colours: grey, pink and heather colours
  - Accent colours: dark or cobalt blue, black and purple
  - Highlight colours: silver and ivory
  - Colour washes: soft pink, lilac, turquoise and peach.

> Top Tip: A bright fuchsia pink, carefully applied either as a wash, shadow or liner, can really brighten blue eyes and make them stand out.

- If you have early stage skin, use the fact that your face doesn't need a lot of make-up to experiment with colour.
- If you have mid/later stage skin, warmer shades will liven up the appearance of your skin and a slight shimmer will be more flattering than anything that is completely matt.

How to apply

- For a full make-up, eye shadow would come after everything else that has already been mentioned in this chapter. For a quick make-up, eyes can be done after any blemishes or dark circles have been concealed and set with powder and after brows have been groomed – always do the brows first, because once the brows are done, sometimes the eyes don't need quite so much. If you do the brows afterwards, sometimes the whole effect can be too heavy.

> Top Tip: Help to make eye shadow stay on longer by gently dusting the eyelid with face powder to absorb any excess oil or moisture.

- This guide is for basic definition of the eye, creating a look that will subtly enhance and flatter everyone without looking too 'done'. It can be done using either cream or powder eye shadow. Creams are good for a quick, natural look, powders can take a bit longer and are better it you want something a bit more polished looking.

- *The base coat* Cover the whole eye area, lash line to brow, with a wash of a pale neutral colour, in a similar tone to your actual skin tone. From the basic palette mentioned above, this would be the bone colour. If using powders, I would use the large flat eye shadow brush to apply this.

- *The shaping* Apply the taupe colour (or equivalent) to the upper and lower lash lines and in the crease of the socket (see Figure 2.23). If using powders, I would use the smaller stiffer 'pencil' style brush for the most precision, and then blend all the edges away using the blending brush.

> Top Tip: Make sure that the brush isn't overloaded by tapping the stem of the brush off on the back of your hand to remove any excess powder.

- *The definition* Using the same stiff 'pencil' style brush, apply your darkest colour, in this case the brown, along the upper lash line, to the outer corner of the eye and a slight sweep at the outer corner of the lower lash line.

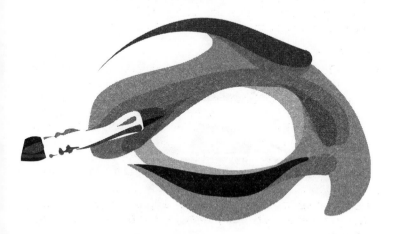

figure 2.23 eyeshadow shaping

- *To finish* A dab of a shimmery shadow blended into the centre of the lid (see Figure 2.24) and under the brow creates the highlight (see Figure 2.25) and a touch of eyeliner pencil smudged and blended at the outer corner of the upper lash line creates the final bit of shading, resulting in a perfectly defined natural-looking eye ready for mascara (see the section on eyelash enhancing, page 160).

Top Tip: To really open up the eyes, use the trick that almost all make-up artists use: dab a little bit of a pale shimmer shadow or highlighter at the inner corner of the eye (see Figure 2.26).

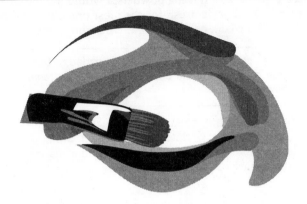

figure 2.24 highlight lid

figure 2.25 highlight under brow

figure 2.26 highlight inner corner of eye

- Customize this basic look by mixing in or replacing these tones with others that you might want to try. For example: on brown eyes, you might want to mix a little pink with the taupe or replace the bone with a champagne colour; on green or hazel eyes you might want to replace the taupe with a khaki or mix the brown with a forest green; on blue eyes you might want to mix the bone with a heather or replace the ivory with a silver.

> Top Tip: If you have very small eyes, stay away from shades that are too dark. Dark colours around small eyes can make them look even smaller. Stick with lighter colours and just the first two steps of base and shape, and then leave out define. Do add in highlighter though, as this draws more light into the eye area, which will make them seem bigger.

- How to apply a smoky eye is explained in the 'smoky eye' section of 'step-by-step make-up looks' (page 182) and eyeliner is explained in the 'movie star' section (page 177). There are also more tips and tricks in the section on professional tips and tricks (page 187).

Eyelash enhancing

Enhancing your eyelashes cannot only add the finishing touch to already made-up eyes, it can work perfectly well all on its own to frame the eyes and make them appear bigger. Applying mascara to the lashes adds energy to the eyes making them look more open and reinforcing their essential femininity. It doesn't matter if you are going for super sophistication or girl-next-door natural, having lovely lashes will bring out the beauty in your eyes and release your inner sparkle.

Whether your natural lashes are short, straight, thin, or even thick and curly, there are mascaras and tools for every situation meaning that it is possible for everyone to have the fullest most flirty flutter possible!

- *Eyelash curlers* Eyelash curlers come in various forms. The one with which most people are familiar is the traditional clamp style that curls the whole set of lashes in one go. Other forms which are available are battery-operated heated eyelash curlers that you press against the lashes, curling them up while the heat 'sets' them, and smaller versions of the clamp style that just curl a few lashes at a time – great for if you are put off by the larger clamp style, or for if you want to give specific lashes an extra lift. If, like me, you have straight eyelashes, some form of eyelash curler is an absolute essential in your make-up kit, because even without mascara, you can use them to make your eyes look instantly more open, more wide awake and more sexy. Curled eyelashes can be like an instant eye-lift.

> Top Tip: A make-up artist trick for if you don't have an eyelash curler to hand but you still want to curl your lashes, is to curl them using the edge of a teaspoon. Hold the lashes between your thumb and the edge of a tea spoon (with your thumb 'in' the spoon bit) and then pressing gently, run the spoon along the lashes to the tips, curling as you go – it's a bit like making gift wrapping ribbon curls using the edge of a pair of scissors, only much gentler – press too hard and you might pull your lashes out, so be careful!

- *Wand mascara* Wand mascara usually comes in a tube with a wand inside which you use to apply it. The wands come in a wide variety of sizes and shapes ranging from curved ones, to big fat ones, to skinny ones that look more like combs.

Wand decoder:

- *Curved* These follow the natural shape of the eye, so you can coat all the lashes in one go. This makes them quick and easy to use. They are often matched with curling formulas for extra lift.
- *Straight* These are easier for adding more layers to specific parts of the lashes, like the outer corner.
- *Closely packed bristles* These coat more lashes at once, depositing a light even coat of mascara and are better for lengthening the lashes.
- *Widely space bristles* These deposit more mascara to lashes with each stroke and are therefore good for volumizing the lashes.
- *Comb style* These apply and separate in one go.

- *Cake mascara* Cake mascara is not as easy to use as wand mascara and takes a bit of practice to get right, but its effects are equally dramatic. It usually comes with a stiff brush that needs to be dampened before you rub it in the block of mascara. You paint the mascara on in the same way that you would with a wand and because you have much more control over how much you put on the brush, it can be much easier to avoid clumps.
- *Mascara primer* Mascara primers are like foundation for lashes. They can add volume, length and staying power to any mascara. Apply in exactly the same way that you apply mascara and make sure that the primer is dry before you apply your first coat of mascara.
- *False eyelashes* False eyelashes can either be a full set, or clumps of 'single' lashes that you glue onto your eyelids to enhance the look of your own lashes. They come in loads of different shapes, lengths and sizes to create anything from natural looking to super glamorous showgirl lashes. They can be a bit tricky to apply, but if you follow my guide, you should have all the tricks you need to make it as easy as possible.

Getting the formula right:

- *Thickening/volumizing mascaras* usually have quite a thick, heavy formula which plumps the lashes up. These work well on thin or fine lashes.
- *Lengthening mascaras* usually have a light formula that dries quickly, which makes it easy to apply a few coats, gradually building up the length of your lashes. These work well if you have short lashes.

- *Waterproof mascaras* can also have any of the above properties, but should also stay in place if they get wet. They are good for weddings, funerals, graduations, sad movies and sometimes even swimming. Because they are waterproof they are also harder to clean off, so you may need to use a special eye make-up remover. They can also be quite drying, so I wouldn't recommend wearing them every day.

- *Treatment/conditioning mascaras* are often fortified with vitamins, moisturizers and proteins that condition and protect the lashes and help stop them from breaking. These are especially good if you suffer from weak lashes and you find that other mascaras tend to dry out your lashes out and make them brittle.

- *Curling mascaras* contain particles that shrink once they are applied to the lashes, which act as a curling mechanism. They are good for an extra bit of lift, or for those of you who don't fancy the idea of trying to curl your lashes with an eyelash curler.

Getting the shade right

- If I could only have one shade of mascara in my kit, I would definitely choose a black one. Black mascara can work on absolutely everyone.

- Brown can also work on everyone but is much more subtle. It is great for natural looks but it can lack the impact and dazzle of a black mascara.

- Aubergine mascara is my recommendation as an alternative to brown, it's a great choice for a natural look with a twist and looks especially good on blonde lashes.

- Bright colours like blue and green, or sparkly silvers and bronzes are great fun but often don't work to lengthen the lashes and open the eyes as much as darker colours do.

> Top Tip: To get the best of both worlds with colours, apply your dark mascara as usual, wait for it to dry and then try just applying the coloured one to the tips of your lashes – kind of like highlights!

- Clear mascara adds a bit of definition to lashes without affecting the length or volume. It is great if you have really sensitive eyes, or for creating super-subtle barely-there make-up looks. It can also double as a way to hold wayward eyebrows in place!

How to curl your eyelashes

- If you have naturally curly lashes, you don't need to read this section. If like me, you have super straight eyelashes (mine even actually grow downwards!) – learning to use an eyelash curler can be a life-changing experience!
- Curl lashes before applying mascara to avoid the risk of breaking them.
- Start by positioning the curler as close to the lash line as possible without pinching your skin (see Figure 2.27).
- Squeeze gently for a couple of seconds, then 'walk' the curler along the lashes a bit and squeeze again. Keep going till you reach the end of your lashes (see Figure 2.27). This walking action ensures a soft curl as opposed to a stiff, square bend.
- If your lashes curl easily, this might be all you need to do. Mine are quite stubborn and I usually have to do this two, or three times to get a good lift. (I also do it a few times just to make sure that they don't fall down again as soon as I put any mascara on!)

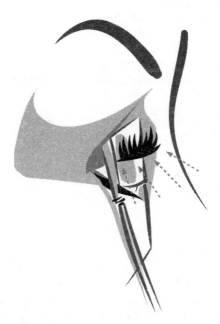

figure 2.27 eyelash curling

Top Tip: You can heat your eyelash curlers by blasting them with your hairdryer for a few seconds and the heat will set the curl better – but be really careful if you try this, because the metal part that touches the eyelid can get really hot and the last thing you want to do is burn your eyelid.

How to apply mascara

- In order to get the best possible mascara application, you need to be sitting still. Apart from it being tricky to get even and keep from making mess, if you are not stationary, it can also be dangerous.

Top Tip: For a bit of extra staying power, lightly dust the lashes with a bit of face powder first, to give your mascara something to cling to.

- Load your wand by twisting it in the tube, not pumping it, as this only fills the tube with air that will dry your mascara out faster. Then dab it on a tissue to remove any massive clumps before they go anywhere near your eye.

Top Tip: If you are going to do them as well, the lower lashes are best done before the upper ones to avoid the risk of transferring mascara onto your eye when you look up. Make sure there isn't too much mascara on the wand and look up, then stroke it gently over the tips of your lower lashes. This should be all you need to do to give them a bit of subtle definition.

- Start by holding the brush horizontally and then position it under the top lashes as close to the roots as possible, twirling the wand slightly to actually 'catch' the lashes in the bristles of the brush.
- Instead of just painting the mascara on in one fluid sweep, wiggle the brush back and forth as you sweep it outwards. This makes sure that not only are the underside of the lashes evenly covered, but also the sides – giving length and volume all in one!
- A second coat will add extra drama, and is best done before the first coat is completely dry. Concentrate the application on the outer two-thirds of the lashes.

- If there are any clumpy bits that you want to get rid of, comb through the lashes to separate them, using a lash comb, before the mascara has dried.

> Top Tip: If you don't have a lash comb, an old mascara wand that has been cleaned of any mascara residue will work just fine (it can also double as an eyebrow grooming brush).

- If a bit of mascara has ended up on your eyelid or underneath your eye, take a cotton bud and gently 'roll' it over the mistake. Keep lifting it off and rolling again until it has lifted off – don't rub it as you will just rub it in and make an even worse mess.

> Top Tip: Make lashes look even longer by 'colouring in' the gaps between the roots of the lashes with some eyeliner, either with a pencil, pen or painted on with an eyeliner brush so that it blends in with the mascara.

- Always take off your mascara at the end of the day – leaving it on can dry the lashes out and they can get brittle and break.

How to apply false eyelashes

- False eyelashes can be quite daunting so if you want to try them, it's worth having a couple of practice goes at it before you do it for real – just to get the hang of it.
- Before you do anything, hold one of the sets of lashes on top of your own to see if the base is actually too long to fit on your eye (this is often the case). If so, you will need to trim them a bit. I usually do this at the outside edge of the false lashes, because the inside corner always tapers down neatly to blend in with your own.

> Top Tip: You can cut a set of false eyelashes in half and just apply them to the outer corners for a bit of a flirty flutter. This works especially well combined with liquid eyeliner. Just make sure that you pair up the two inner halves as one pair and the two outer halves as another – they will be slightly different from each other and if you a pair them up wrongly, you will have wonky lashes.

- Apply a bit of eyelash glue to the back of you hand and let it start to dry for a minute or two so that it becomes tacky. You will know when it is ready to use because the edge will have changed colour slightly. If you don't wait for the glue to get tacky, the lashes will slide all over the place when you try to apply them, they won't adhere immediately and the glue will go everywhere and make a mess.

- Bend the base of the lashes slightly so that they are a little more curved before you apply the glue – this makes them easier to apply and also less likely to peel off. Then, using the end of an eyeshadow brush, carefully apply a line of glue along the edge of the base of one set of lashes.

- Close or look down with the eye that you are applying onto first, and start by sticking down the outer edge right on the natural lash line. If the glue is tacky enough, it should hold well enough for you to gently press the rest of it into place. Gently press along the edge with the tip of an eyeshadow brush to make sure that it is stuck down properly. Then apply the other side.

- Once the glue has dried, carefully paint over the join with some eyeliner. Apply mascara to blend the false lashes in with your own real ones.

> Top Tip: Instead of the glue that comes in the packet with the eyelashes, I prefer to use a surgical adhesive that dries black instead of clear, which saves having to paint over the dry glue rim with eyeliner to cover the join.

- To remove them, gently pull them away from the eyelid, being careful not to pull your own eyelashes as well. If you are worried about it this, you can dissolve the glue by applying a little make-up remover first. If you want to reuse them, clean all the glue and mascara off first, and don't forget to clean any glue off any brushes or tools that you used to apply them.

- Singles are applied in exactly the same way, except for the fact that you apply them one at a time, concentrating on the outer two-thirds of the eye. For them to look as natural as possible, they need to go directly between your natural lashes.

Luscious lips

Like eye make-up, lipstick can have amazing transformative powers. There's nothing like a coat of lipstick to give yourself an instant boost of confidence, and trying out a new colour can change your whole look. One slick can take you from serene to sophisticated or from virgin to vixen. You might prefer a dab of balm and a smudge of colour that hints at a more sultry allure, or a glossy 'Va va voom' pout might be your preference. Whichever it is, there is something for everyone.

Lipsticks are available in a myriad of styles, textures and finishes and just like most other make-up, modern formulas often contain all kinds of active ingredients, like vitamin E, aloe vera, collagen and sunscreen, that can make them become extensions of your skin care. Hopefully this guide can help you to find the type, formula and shade that is right for you and for the look that you want to create.

- *Lip balm* Lip balms are used to seal moisture into the lips and can be applied either using fingers or a lip brush. As explained in the skin-care section, lips have no natural sebum to hold in moisture or melanin to protect them from the sun, so they are very prone to being dehydrated, chapped and sunburned. Therefore, in order to get the best out of your lip balm, use one that has at least SPF 15 and wear it over a layer of moisturizer. Lip balms are also available with tint in them, which can be a less sticky and more muted alternative to lip gloss, great for barely-there make-up looks.

> Top Tip: Don't forget that sleep is very dehydrating for the body, especially the mouth, so slather on the lip balm (over some moisturizer) before you go to bed, to prevent waking up in the morning with dry and flaky lips.

- *Lipstick* Lipstick is the traditional way to add colour to the lips. The twist-up stick is the most recognizable form of lipstick, but you can also find lipstick in pots, palettes and pen or wand style dispensers. They can range from anywhere between smooth and creamy to sheer and waxy. They can leave anything from a stain that stays on all day to just a hint of colour, depending on your preference. They can be applied directly to the lips, or they can be applied using fingers or a lip brush. Each type of application will get a different-looking result. Straight from the tube will usually get the most colour and is good for a speedy result. Using fingers gives a subtle, soft finish and is perfect for natural or nonchalant make-up looks, and is a great way to wear a bold colour without it being too 'done'. Using a lip brush gives a lot of control. You can be very precise about where you apply also and about how much you apply.

- *Lip pencil* Lip pencils can be either thin or chunky. The thin ones are generally used to line the lip, enhancing its outline, and are usually a tiny bit stiffer and waxier than the chunky ones, which are usually softer and creamier and work more like a lipstick. Lip liners give not only definition, but they can also help to stop lipstick from bleeding or feathering – especially with reds and dark colours. A nude pencil is a must-have if you have later stage skin.

> Top Tip: Lip liner should either be lip coloured (i.e. nude) or it should match your lipstick. I save the dark-liner and pale-lipstick look for porn stars and drag queens.

- *Lip gloss* Lip glosses add shine to the lips. Shine draws in more light and so, like highlighter, it works to not only attract more attention to the lips by lighting them up, it also draws them forward, making them appear fuller. Lip glosses can be clear, tinted or have extra sparkle to give the illusion of even more fullness. They can be worn alone for a soft look, they can be worn with liner for extra definition, or they can be layered over lipstick (and liner) for the complete works – which is great for really polished make-up looks or if you are being photographed. They can be applied directly onto the lips, dabbed on with fingers, or painted on with a brush. If you have full lips and you want to play them down, avoid glosses altogether, as they will just make them look even fuller.

- *Lip stains* Lip stains come in many forms. They can look like pens or pencils, they can also sometimes look worryingly similar to nail polishes (be careful getting those mixed up!) and they can also come in tubes or pots. But whatever the packaging, they all do the same thing. They deposit a colour on the lips that 'stains' it and stays all day – if you apply using your finger, make sure to wash your hands straight away. They are great for low-maintenance looks, and also for on holiday – you can layer them under SPF lipbalm for a look that can even go in the pool!

Get the formula right

- *Cream* This is your regular, no-frills lipstick. It should be smooth, creamy and easy to apply and will work for everyone. If it is labelled 'moisturizing' it will help the lips to seal in moisture (like a lip balm), but may not stay on for long. They can sometimes contain shimmer for a bit of highlight, creating the illusion of a bit more fullness. This texture is great if you have later stage skin.

- *Sheer* These tend to be lighter weight than cream formulas. They don't deposit as much colour onto the lips, but they are more real-looking in appearance. Great for natural and barely-there make-up looks, but they don't have much staying power. Like creams, they can also contain shimmer for highlight and the illusion of fullness.
- *Matt* Matt formulas are like cream formulas with no shine at all, and can be a bit drier in texture. They need to have very smooth lips underneath them as chapped lips will only look ten times worse with matt lipstick on top of them. They can, however, look extremely sophisticated either as part of a 'look' or even just on their own as a statement. If you have small lips, avoid matt formulas unless you are going to layer gloss on top of them.

> Top Tip: If you have a matt lipstick and you love the colour, but the texture is too heavy, you can apply lip balm to your lips and then dab a bit of your matt lipstick on with your finger for a much softer feel.

- *Extra long wear* Extra long-wear lipsticks are like a cross between a lipstick and a stain. They have a lot of colour pigment in them to give them the extra staying power. Their texture can be quite dry and because of this they are usually accompanied by either a gloss or a balm. Like matt formulas, they don't look so good on chapped lips. They are great for make-up looks that need to stay on for a long time – for weddings, for example – but they don't work so well for soft, natural looks. A more natural-looking alternative to a long-wear lipstick is a lip stain (see above) which 'tints' the lips rather than 'painting' them.

> Top Tip: Waterproof mascara remover will usually also take off long-wear lipstick.

Get the shade right

It is really difficult to say that certain colours will work well on you if you have this skin tone or that hair colour, because the choice of colours and tones is so extensive. In an attempt to give a starting point, here is some information about what I think are the three main lipstick colour groups: nudes, reds and pinks. To really know what you are going to get though, you need to test them out. They look different in the tube than they do on the lips, and also people's own body chemistry can make lipsticks change slightly – so a shade that looks one way on one person can look very different on somebody else.

Top Tip: Don't test lipsticks on the back of your hand – your lips aren't that colour. I also don't recommend trying shop testers on your lips unless the sales assistants are hygiene conscious and you know that the lipsticks haven't already been tried on by every other person walking by. A good thing to remember is that the pads of your fingers usually have a bit more blood closer to the surface, making them a bit more pink in colour and therefore closer to the colour of your lips.

- *Nudes* The right shade of nude lipstick is a perfect, everyday, all-occasions colour. It can look either natural or sophisticated, or even both all at the same time, depending on the rest of the make-up and how it is applied! For something that looks natural, avoid anything too matt and go for something that matches your natural lip colour. Fairer skins look better with more pinky- or peachy-toned nude shades and warmer or darker skins can also go for sandy- or toffee-toned shades as well.
- *Reds* Red lipstick makes a statement. It says confidence, style and sophistication. Red lips can add glamour to any make-up look and can work just as well with jeans and a t-shirt as they can with a party dress. For a perfectly polished pout, red lipstick needs to be carefully applied and maintained, but it can look just as good dabbed on with fingers for a softer more natural look. Reds can range from being either warm and orange-toned to being cool and blue-toned. If your complexion suits cool colours, then a cool red will work better for you. If your complexion suits warm colours, then a warm red will work better for you. Whether cool or warm colours suit you isn't necessarily down to your skin colour. I have warm, olive skin but I suit cool colours better and on me, a cool red looks much more flattering than a warm red.

  If you want to make a statement, but you feel that red is a little too bold for you, then deep wine colours like burgundy and plum have a similar wow factor, but they don't shout it quite so loud. They also flatter most skin tones. Avoid reds and darker shades if you have small or thin lips, because they will just end up looking thinner.

Top Tip: If you have dark skin and you want to tone down a bright red, you can add a touch of brown to make it a bit more wearable (cream bronzer or brown lipstick will work well).

- *Pinks* Pink lipstick is often written off as being too cute or girlie, but I use pale petal pink lipsticks more than any others in my kit. They always look soft and pretty and can really brighten up a dull complexion. Sheer or creamy formulas work better than shimmery or matt ones, and mixed with a dab of gloss can give fantastically full-looking lips. Brighter pinks like fuchsia are a great alternative to red and look equally amazing on paler skins as they do on darker skins. The best way to wear a bright pink like this, though, is to keep the rest of the face really simple, to avoid it looking overdone.

Top Tip: If you have later stage skin, try soft peachy or rosy pinks on the lips as dark shades will emphasize thinning lips and feathery lines.

How to apply
- Lipstick never looks good on dry and flaky lips. Make sure that they are in good condition by exfoliating your lips first. My favourite way is to massage a bit of rich moisturizer or lip balm into them with a soft toothbrush – baby ones are great for this. Do this as part of your daily skin care routine.
- After lips have been moisturized, apply lip balm with a finger to seal in the moisture and provide the best base for a good lipstick application. For best result, the lip balm needs to have been on for at least ten minutes, otherwise the lipstick will just slide off again.

Top Tip: As mentioned in the 'base basics' section (page 117), if you moisturize and seal your lips before you start doing your foundation, by the time you get to applying lipstick, your lip balm will have settled nicely and your lipstick should glide on easily.

- To help your lipstick or gloss stay on for longer, give them something to grab onto by dusting your lips lightly with face powder first. Make sure there is no excess as this will just form a paste!

- If you have dark skin and want to even out the tone of your lips before you start, apply and blend a little foundation or concealer onto the lips before you apply any colour.
- This guide is for a 'the full works': lipstick, liner and gloss. Pick out the bits you need, but if you are just doing gloss and liner, I would do the gloss first (as if it were lipstick) and then line the lips afterwards for the most natural-looking finish.
  - Start with lipstick. As mentioned above, applying with a brush gives you the most precision with where and how you place it. Two thin layers applied with a brush will last longer than one thick layer applied directly from the stick. Paint the lipstick on from the centre of the mouth outwards. Extend the colour all the way to your natural lip line.
  - The best way to ensure that your lipstick stays in place is to blot this layer with a tissue and then reapply another layer. For even more staying-power, dust a little face powder over the tissue before you peel it away.
  - Then use a lip pencil to define the lip line and make any adjustments to the shape. By waiting until you already have your lipstick applied, your lip liner is much easier to apply, it will look more natural and it is much easier to see exactly where any corrections might need to be made. For basic definition, start at the centre of your upper lip and draw a line to each outer corner, following the edge of your natural lip line.
- To make lips appear fuller, do the same as for the basic definition (above) but nudge the lip line out slightly, following your own shape. Don't go more than one pencil line width over the natural lip line. This will give you a natural extension, and if you eat the lipstick off, you are not left with too much of an unnatural looking line.
- To correct uneven lips, line the fuller side first as normal, and then nudge out the thinner side to match.
- Cover up any smudges or bleeding with a cotton bud dipped in concealer or a concealer pencil.

Top Tip: Keeping lip pencils in the fridge makes it easier to sharpen them without them falling apart. If they are then a bit too stiff to draw on your lips, you can warm them up by drawing on the back of your hand.

- Finish off with either a full coat of gloss, or just a dab in the centre of the lower lip to plump it up.

Step-by-step make-up looks

Basic face (Plate 1)

I call this the 'get out of jail face' – it's like the 'get out of jail free' card in Monopoly – if you've got one of these up your sleeve, it will get you out of trouble every time, without fail. All the other looks described here are great for specific situations; at a push, if you could only do this one, you would be fine every time. It is basically about making yourself as beautiful as possible with as little make-up as you can get away with.

Use the pointers below together with the detailed instructions from the previous sections to work out your own personal basic face. To help you remember everything you can fill in your specific information in the basic face chart (Plate 2).

The *key words* for this look are simple, effortless, natural, healthy and enhanced, but not 'done'.

The *colour palette* for this look is neutral, natural-looking colours that are close to your natural skin tones. Warm rather than cool tones for a fresh healthy look work well on everyone. Sheer neutral tones, like browns, caramels and rose colours, flatter every skin tone, and if you use these shades you won't look like you are trying too hard.

The *textures* for this look are as lightweight and sheer as possible. Creams and liquids will give the most subtle effect, powders applied delicately and carefully will give a more professional looking finish.

The basic face can be done in three ways. You can stick to just one, or you can mix and match to suit your mood:

- *Super natural* – the quickest and most minimal. It is young and fresh looking.
- *Barely there* – involves very subtle enhancement, for a natural but modern look.
- *Naturally perfect* – the 'no make-up' look, so that you look like you, only better, and people still see you before they see your make-up.

Base

- *Super natural*: none, or tinted moisturizer
- *Barely there*: tinted moisturizer or base just where it's needed
- *Naturally perfect*: tinted moisturizer or base just where it's needed if your skin is good, otherwise, a sheer application all over.

Concealer

For all looks, apply concealer where necessary.

Powder

- *Super natural*: not necessary unless you have oily skin, in which case a light dusting to prevent shine
- *Barely there* and *naturally perfect*: just a sheer veil to set the make-up and keep everything in its place.

Brows

- *Super natural* and *Barely there*: shaped is enough
- *Naturally perfect*: shaped and lightly filled.

Highlighter

- *Super natural*: not necessary, but is a nice extra and wouldn't look overdone if blended well
- *Barely there* and *Naturally perfect*: very subtly applied and blended to the C shape around the eyes, to lift and define the cheekbones.

Bronzer

- *Super natural*: not necessary
- *Barely there*: not necessary unless you feel a bit washed-out
- *Naturally perfect*: a light dusting to warm the complexion.

Blusher

For all three looks, applying a warm tone of blusher wakes up the face by giving it a healthy flush.

Eyes

- *Super natural*: just apply mascara
- *Barely there*: try a colour wash and mascara
- *Naturally perfect*: define the eyes, not too darkly, blending away all harsh edges, and add mascara.

Lips

For all three looks, the lips will come down to your own personal choice. The following lists all the finishes in approximate order of colour density (from least dense to most dense):

- lip balm, clear lip gloss
- tinted lip balm, tinted lip gloss
- sheer lipstick, lipstick dabbed on with a finger over lip-balm
- lip stain (with or without balm or gloss on top), lipstick applied and then blotted, lipstick applied with a finger with gloss on top
- cream lipstick (in two layers)
- lipstick with gloss on top
- matt lipstick/ long-wear lipstick.

Bride (Plate 3)

My 'bride' look is like an extension of the basic face. It should make you look special without being unrecognizable. If the basic face is meant to look like you only better, then the 'bride' is you at your best. The skin should be flawless and glowing, the eyes sparkling and the cheeks should be flushed – emphasizing all the signs that the face displays when we are in love. Because it is timeless, this look is not just for brides, it works for any special occasion where you still want to look natural, and is great if you need to be photographed for any reason. The make-up should be lightweight and natural-looking while at the same time enhancing the skin tone, covering blemishes and highlighting all the features enough so that nothing gets lost in the photographs. Flash photography especially can drain the colour out of faces, so a 'super natural' or 'barely there' face might appear naked and a bit washed out in pictures. Use the pointers below together with the detailed instructions given in the previous sections to work out your own personal 'bride' face. To help you remember everything you can fill in your specific information in the 'bride' face chart (Plate 4).

The *key words* for this look are soft, sheer, delicate, pretty and radiant.

The *colour palette* for this look is either neutral warms, like the basic face, but can also be neutral cools (adding greys and charcoals around the eyes and a cooler petal pink on the lips). Whatever the colour scheme for the wedding is, the make-up should match the face and not necessarily the colour scheme.

Although, as mentioned in the 'shadow secrets' section (page 152), there is lots of room to experiment with the basic definition, adding more interesting shades if so desired.

The *textures* for this look are smooth, iridescent, lightweight but long-lasting. Creams and liquids will give a very natural looking finish, but powders will stay on longer and give a more intensity of colour.

> Top Tip: Avoid having a facial or using a face mask for three days before the big day so as not to run the risk of drawing any impurities to the surface.

Base

For staying power and photography purposes, apply a full face of foundation, but make it sheer so that it doesn't feel heavy on the face. Avoid pink-toned foundations as they don't look as good as neutral yellow tones in photographs. To be absolutely sure that your base doesn't move, use a primer beforehand. Primers are explained in the professional tips and tricks at the end of the chapter (page 187). For an extra bit of radiance, try using a base or primer (but not both) that contains light-reflecting particles, or you could mix a bit of highlighter in with one of them. Go easy though, too much 'radiance' can just become 'shiny', which isn't pretty any more.

Concealer

Apply concealer where necessary. Don't forget the outer corner of the eyes, the crease of the nose and the outer corners of the mouth for a really flawless finish.

Powder

Set the base, concealer (and any other cream formulations) in place with a generous dusting of powder, but make sure to sweep away all the excess, especially from under the eyes. Pay extra attention to the forehead and just above the upper lip, which are the first places that will start to show any signs of shine.

Brows

Brows should be shaped and filled, but not too heavily: just enough to frame the face nicely, and draw all the focus into the eyes.

Highlighter

Dab and blend highlighter in the C shape around the eyes to lift
the cheekbones and brow bones and bring more light into the
eye area.

Bronzer

A light dusting of bronzer, applied to all the places where the
sun hits the face, will warm the complexion and subtly define
the features.

Blusher

A soft rosy pink blended upwards and outwards from the apple
of the cheek adds a beautiful soft flush. Add a swirl at the
temples and on the ears – especially if you are wearing your
hair up.

Eyes

Basic definition using either a warm neutral palette (bone,
taupe, brown) or a cool neutral palette (bone, grey, charcoal)
softly blended and highlighted with shimmer at the inner corner,
on the middle of the lid and under the brow. Don't forget the
waterproof mascara.

Lips

My personal favourite for most brides is a soft petal pink, but
lipstick can be such a personal thing. As mentioned in the
'luscious lips' section (page 166), you can never go wrong with
a colour that matches your natural lip colour, but remember
that photography can sometimes drain colour a little, and that
something a little brighter may photograph better. I prefer the
soft look of a sheer lip colour coated with a layer of gloss, but
this isn't always practical for brides and it would require regular
retouching. If the lipstick really needs to stay put for a long time,
you could go for a long-wear formula but make sure that the
lips are well prepared and moisturized beforehand to help stop
them from drying out too much. Alternatively you could use the
lipliner base trick as described in the professional tips and tricks
at the end of the chapter.

Movie star (Plate 5)

This is a look for someone who wants to be noticed. It is perfect
for red carpet events because it is chic, dramatic and it
photographs perfectly: accentuating all the features of the face,

while at the same time not looking overdone in reality. Female film icons like Audrey Hepburn, Marilyn Monroe, Sophia Loren and Brigette Bardot continue to inspire us to recreate this classic statement look. Use the pointers below together with the detailed instructions from the previous sections to work out your own personal 'movie star' face. To help you remember everything you can fill in your specific information in the 'movie star' face chart (Plate 6).

The *key words* for this look are classic, sophisticated, elegant and seductive.

The *colour palette* for this look is: a cool neutral palette either using a soft wash of something silvery or a combination of bone, grey and charcoal tones to define very subtly the eyes with a hint of cool blush on the cheeks. The lips are bold and either traffic-stopping red or a deep dark wine colour.

The *textures* for this look are satin, silk, rich and creamy.

Base

A perfect base is the key to this look. Something with a more satin or matt texture will give the skin a more sophisticated look.

Concealer

Apply concealer where necessary. Don't forget the outer corner of the eyes, the crease of the nose and the outer corners of the mouth for a flawless finish. Red lips will highlight any other red on your face, so this is extra important for this look.

Powder

Powder is very important to set the base and concealer and also to keep any shine at bay. Sweaty and sophisticated don't work together at all!

Brows

Brows should be shaped and perfectly filled. The classic movie stars always had perfect eyebrows. Dramatic liner draws attention to the eyes, making brows more noticeable – so keep brows well groomed if you want to go for this look.

Highlighter

Dab and blend highlighter in the C shape around the eyes to lift the cheekbones and brow bones and bring more light into the eye area.

Top Tip: Don't forget exposed skin on shoulders, arms and *décolleté*. Make sure to moisturize and add shimmer for the final touch of Hollywood glamour.

Bronzer

To keep the coolness of this look, leave the bronzer out completely. Definition can be created using blusher.

Blusher

Use two tones of blusher to create natural but elegant cheeks. Define the cheekbones by sweeping underneath it with a cool deep tone (something similar to the tone of your natural 'blush'). Then add a brighter more pinky tone at the apples of the cheeks, or higher up on the cheekbones, blending both colours upwards and outwards towards the hairline and down towards to jaw. Dust what is left on the brush at the temples.

Eyes

This look is a combination of very subtle colour on the eyes teamed with a slick of eyeliner to add drama and allure. The base of the eye is either a gentle wash of something light and shimmery, or soft definition using a cool palette of bone, grey and charcoal. If you are going for the definition, keep it subtle, it is only meant to be the backdrop for the real definition which comes with the eyeliner. Don't forget to finish with lashings of mascara.

How to apply eyeliner

The classic 'movie star' eyeliner is a line painted along the entire top lash line that extends slightly at the corners. It can be done using liquid eyeliner, a pen liner, a gel or dark eye shadow and a damp eyeliner brush or a pencil – either way, the technique is pretty much the same. Pencil is the easiest, but also the softest effect. Painting with a pen, a shadow or gel liner requires only a little more effort for a stronger result. The most difficult is lining the eye using a liquid liner, because keeping it even takes confidence and a steady hand. With a little practice and this guide it can be easily mastered and the dramatic results are well worth the effort.

- If the lids don't already have any sort of powder eye shadow on them, give them a light dusting of face powder.
- Load your brush and gently blot it on a tissue to remove any excess.

Top Tip: Do a couple of practice strokes on your hand so that you not only feel in control, but so that you can see the density of colour. If it isn't dense enough, you may want to add some more.

- In order to have the most control, sit at a table with the elbow of your drawing arm on the table to stop it from wobbling. Hold a hand/compact mirror in the other hand, place it under your chin and look down into it. This way, you can clearly see the whole of your lashline without having to scrunch up your eye. You are also not battling to paint through your eyelashes (see Figure 2.30).
- Holding your brush as if it were a pencil and so that it is angled downward, into the lashes, keep it as close to the lash line as possible and do one of the following:
  - *Pro* Start at the inner corner and sweep in one continuous movement all the way across to the outer corner.
  - *Novice* Place the brush at the middle of your eye and paint from the middle to the outer corner and then from the inner corner to the middle.
  - *Beginner* Start from the inner corner and draw small, connected dashes along the top lash line.

figure 2.28 apply eyeliner

- Once the first line is on, you can go over it, to either thicken, darken or tidy it up. It is important to make sure that the liner goes as close to the roots of the lashes as possible so that there is no skin visible between the lashes and the liner. You can increase the definition even more by painting in between the eyelashes (but this can be slightly easier to do with a pencil). Traditionally, the line should be thin at the inner and outer corner and slightly thicker in the middle.

> Top Tip: Use less pressure at the inner corner so that the line can gradually fade and become thinner.

- To create a flick at the outer edge, place your mirror down on the table and look down into it. Use your free hand to pull the corner of your eyebrow upwards and outwards until your eyelid is taut, then extend your liner upwards and outwards following the natural shape of your lashes. The flick is designed to look like extra lashes in the corner of your eyes, so if your lashes are long and curly, angle the line upwards more towards the temple; if they are straighter and shorter, keep it flatter.
- Once you have finished painting, close the eye and try to keep it closed for at least ten seconds to give it time to dry – you will need longer if you have painted a thick or heavy line.
- Correct any mistakes with a cotton bud dipped in a tiny amount of eye make-up remover (too much and it will ruin the good bits, so be careful). Cotton buds with pointed tips are especially good for this.

> Top Tip: For extra intensity and/or staying power, you can go over your line with a dry line of fine black powder shadow, but be sure to use the tissue trick described in professional tips and tricks (p. 187), to stop any powder from falling onto the face and making a mess.

Eyeliner to suit your eye shape

- *To widen close-set eyes* Only line the outer two-thirds of the upper lid, and extend slightly outwards. Team with highlighter at the inner corner to give the illusion of more space in between.
- *To make small eyes appear bigger* Thicken your line at the outer edge to open them up more. Team with a little highlighter under the outer corner of the lower lashes and at the inner corner of the eye.

- *To lift drooping eyes* Only line outer third of eye very close to lashes and sweep the liner upwards at the outer corner of the eye. Team with subtle definition at the socket and highlighter under the outer brow.
- *To lift deep-set eyes* Avoid too much dark shadow. A really fine line is enough to define deep-set eyes, which are more flattered by soft shimmery shades on the lids and a smudge of a neutral pencil under the lower lashes.

Lips

This look makes a real statement with a bold colour on the lips. Darker pigments magnify any dry or flaky patches on the lips, so make sure to prep well first. If you like the idea of siren red, then go for it! Otherwise go for a deep plum or a burgundy colour that still has wow factor but doesn't shout it quite so loud.

> Top Tip: You can tone down the brightness of any lipstick by mixing in a bit of brown (a cream bronzer or a brown lipstick is good for this).

Follow the steps in the 'luscious lips' section (page 166), to create your perfect pout. Use a matching liner to add extra definition and help stop any bleeding or feathering. For polished sophistication, keep the lips matt looking, add a dab of gloss for the Jessica Rabbit/bombshell look, or, just dab on a bit of colour with a fingertip for a more nonchalant version.

Smoky eye (Plate 7)

The allure of the smoky eye lies in the dark halo effect that seems to entice and mesmerize by adding depth and dimension. Lashes appear longer and thicker and the whites of the eye appear whiter. The eyes become the unmistakable focal point of the face, but in a very sultry, come-hither sort of way. The smoky eye look can work really well in two completely different ways, depending on the mood you want to create, I call the extremes: 'soft and sultry' or 'rock chick edgy'. Experiment with the different finishes and use the pointers below together with the detailed instructions in the previous chapter to work out your own personal smoky eye look. To help you remember everything you can, fill in your specific information in the smoky eye look chart (Plate 8).

The *key words* for this look are dramatic, mysterious, smouldering and sexy.

The *colour palette* for this look is traditionally the colours of smoke (grey, charcoal and black). Black liner with metallic grey shadow flatters almost everyone, but you can add the dark smoky effect to pretty much any colour eyeshadow by blending a dark colour or black at the lashline. Shimmer shadows work the best to give richness and depth.

The *textures* for this look are velvet, smooth and luxurious.

Base

- *Soft and sultry*: the base needs to be perfect, to draw all the attention to the darkness of the eyes. Keep it more towards a satin or matt finish as anything too dewy will take impact away from the shimmer of the eyes.
- *Rock chick edgy*: has minimal to no base, creating something that looks like you might have already slept in it.

Concealer

For both looks, apply concealer where necessary.

Powder

- *Soft and sultry*: powder is very important to set the base in place and keep any shine at bay
- *Rock chick edgy*: avoid too much powder on the face, but keep the T-zone shine free. Blotting sheets are great for this.

Brows

For both looks, brows should be shaped but not filled. There is enough going on around the eyes – adding dark-filled brows could end up looking too heavy.

Highlighter

For both looks, dab and blend highlighter in a C shape around the eyes. This lifts the cheekbones and brow bones and brings more light into the eyes.

Bronzer

For both looks, bronzer isn't necessary. If the skin is kept pale, it will contrast better with the dark eyes.

Blusher

Dark, dramatic eyes can have a tendency to drain colour out of the rest of the face, so a subtle hint of blusher works well to balance this. Keep it really light though, especially for the rock chick edgy version, because a 'healthy glow' kind of takes away a bit of the edginess.

Eyes

The smoky eye effect can be created in many different ways. I have broken it down into three basic ways that should take fifteen, ten and five minutes to create. Any of the three methods could be used to create either the soft and sultry version, or the rock chick edgy version (just remember that the rock chick version doesn't want to look too perfect) so use the one that suits your style best. If your eyelids are hooded, don't go too dark on your eyelid and make sure to have lots of highlighter under the brow. The key with all three versions is to use a dark liner together with shimmery eyeshadow.

> Top Tip: To help the rock chick edgy version along its way, a dab of eye gloss in the centre of the lid at the end, will help it to look a bit more 'worn in'.

15 minutes

This is the most polished version. It is similar to the basic eye definition as detailed in the 'shadow secrets' section (page 152), with more of the darker shades applied to the eyelid.

- Start by applying your base shadow colour (the lightest one – not too shimmery) over the whole eyelid, all the way up to the brow.
- Apply the next shade over just the lid, blending it away just above the crease of the socket.

> Top Tip: If you have more than one brush, use a clean one for each shade to keep the definition. Otherwise, wipe your brush off on a tissue between each application.

- Shade the socket and upper and lower lash line using your darkest colour and blend so that there are no harsh edges.

> Top Tip: Make sure that your brush isn't overloaded with dark shadow, that can drop down onto your face, by tapping the stem of the brush off on the back of your hand to remove any excess powder.

- Then, using a soft black (or dark) eyeliner pencil, line the edge of the eye, top and bottom as close to the lash line as possible. It doesn't have to be a perfect line, because it's going to get blended. The more liner you add at this stage, the darker and heavier the smoky effect will become. Make sure that the upper and lower liner joins up at the outer corner of the eye.

Top Tip: This look has the most impact when the inner rims of the eyes (both top and bottom) are lined with the pencil, but don't do this if you have sensitive eyes because it can cause irritation. Lessen the risk of irritation by always keeping your pencil clean by sharpening it after every use.

- Blend this pencil line with a second coat of the darkest shadow around the lash line and add more at the outer corner, or at the socket line if you want to deepen the eyes even more.

Top Tip: If at any point you think that the colour is too intense, go over it gently with a cotton bud or take it down slightly by blending in a little face powder.

- Then add in the highlight: a pop of something pale and shimmery blended at the inner corner of the eye, onto the centre of the lid and under the brow.
- The look is completed with a final sweep of pencil liner (or liquid for an even more dramatic effect) for extra definition, and two coats of mascara to the top and bottom lashes.

10 minutes

This is a great way to transform a day look into a night look

- Using the colour palette of your choice, define the eye using the instructions detailed in the 'shadow secrets' section (page 152).
- Using an eye pencil, preferably a chunky one as they are easier to blend, line the whole eye – upper and lower lashes (it doesn't have to be neat) – and dot pencil at the outer corner of the lid and sweep into the socket. If you have small or close-set eyes, just do the outer edges of your eyes and keep the inner edges paler.
- Using a finger, a cotton bud or an eye shadow brush, gently smudge this pencil application so that the edges become soft and fade away to nothing.

- This look has the most impact when the top and bottom inner rims of the eyes are lined with a thin pencil but don't do this if you have sensitive eyes because it can cause irritation. Lessen this risk by always keeping your pencil clean and sharp.

• Then add in the highlight: a pop of something pale and shimmery blended at the inner corner of the eye, onto the centre of the lid and under the brow.

- Finish with two coats of mascara to the top and bottom lashes.

5 minutes

This is a very easy, super speedy way to create a smoky eye effect

- Take a pale shimmery cream shadow and wash it over the whole eyelid, right up to the brow. Use a cotton bud to apply a little under the lower lashline too.

- Use either a chunky or regular eyeliner to cover one of your fingertips (preferably the middle one) with black pencil.

- Carefully dab this finger onto your eyelid, starting at the outer corner and working along the lash line. The pencil will blend with the cream to give a soft smoky effect. Use a cotton bud with some pencil on it to do the same to the lower lashline.

- Repeat this as often as you like – the more layers, the darker and smokier it will get.

- This look has the most impact when the top and bottom inner rims of the eyes are lined with a thin pencil but don't do this if you have sensitive eyes because it can cause irritation. Lessen this risk by always keeping your pencil clean and sharp.

- Finish with two coats of mascara to the top and bottom lashes.

Lips

Lips should be kept pale and simple. A sheer pink lipstick or a slick of gloss is enough to offset the dark dramatic eyes and keep the face in balance.

Professional tips and tricks

On top of everything else that I have already mentioned, there are a few more insider secrets that I thought were worth sharing. I have learned all of these things in my 18 years in the fashion and beauty industry, both as a model and as a make-up artist.

Make-up tips and tricks

- *Foundation primer* The real make-up artist trick to making foundation look better and stay on longer is to apply a foundation primer first. These used to be a real trade secret, but now most make-up companies make their own version. They lock in all your moisturizer and act not only as a barrier to stop your make-up from sinking into your skin, they also help your make-up to stick to your face better. Your foundation will also go on smoother because the primer will have evened out the complexion and filled in any fine lines. Not only that, primers can also help to mattify, tone down redness and add luminosity – or even all three if you need it!

- *Step back* Make sure that you regularly step back from the mirror and check what you have done from a bit of distance – things look totally different when you are close up, and don't forget that the more distant version is what everyone else sees. If at any point you think that maybe you have applied a bit too much, then you probably have. Stepping back frequently can help to prevent this.

- *Make-up bag* Don't carry your whole make-up bag around with you in your handbag – you don't need it all. You really only need a few items for touch-ups. I have a separate smaller bag that just lives in my handbag and in it I have seven things:
  - a compact powder foundation – this has many functions: it works as a mirror, dabbed with a finger it can re-cover any blemishes, with its sponge it can re-touch the base that got eaten off at lunch time, and with a small brush it can be used to dust away any shine
  - a light-reflective concealer – to get rid of any dark circles that might have reappeared!
  - a multi-function 'lip and cheek' product – or a lipstick in a colour that could also work on the cheeks, for reapplying lips and cheeks as necessary
  - a shimmer cream eyeshadow or highlighter – to use on cheeks or eyes

- a lip balm – for re-moisturizing
- a lip gloss – a handbag must-have
- an eyeliner pencil – for just in case I want to change my day look to a night look (as explained in the 'smoky eye' section (page 182).

Because I have curled my lashes and applied mascara before I left the house, I don't need to do that again during the day. You would only need a bronzer in your handbag if you are a bronzer addict – one application in the morning should really be enough to last you all day.

- *Make-up tools* You don't need to spend money on a special brush to groom your brows, or an eyelash comb. Wash out the wand from an old mascara that is past its use-by date (i.e. three months old) and use that for both jobs. Make sure to give it a wipe after combing the lashes though, you don't want to be painting mascara on your eyebrows!

- *Where to spend your money* I would spend money on a good foundation – it is your key to flawless looking skin so it's worth it – so long as it is the right colour for your skin. Take your time and find the perfect one. I would also spend money on a few good brushes as they can really make the difference between a good application and a bad one. I would save money on mascaras and eyeliners. Most high street brands will do the trick just fine, they just won't look as nice if they fall out of your handbag! If image is your thing, then treat yourself to a lovely compact for your handbag as this will be on show more than anything else!

- *Get into sampling* If you are going to be spending money on expensive skin care and make-up, ask if you can take samples home to try them out. There is no point shelling out for an expensive cream or a base only to get home and find that your skin doesn't agree with it, or that you can't live with the smell. If the sales assistant says that they don't have samples but you really want to try something – you can take your own little pot with you (an old, empty, clean pot of eye cream would do) and ask for a couple of squirts to take home and try.

- *Holiday make-up* Healthy, happy holiday skin doesn't need much make-up. The 'super natural' basic face (page 173), done with creams and stains, is all you would need if you wanted anything at all. But holiday time is a perfect time to have fun and experiment with new colours. A flash of vivid green eyeliner, or a slick of hot pink lipstick – very Brazilian! Think tropical, think exotic, be bold – bright colours look amazing with a tan, and even if you don't dare try anything on your face, toe nails are a perfect place to play with hot colours.

- *Concealer know-how* Before you apply your under-eye concealer, look into a flat mirror in front of you and tilt your chin down. You will immediately see which areas are the darkest and need the most correcting.

- *Make-up refresher 1* During the day, especially if it is hot, don't always reach for the powder to tone down any shine – too many layers can leave the face feeling heavy and cakey. A quick spritz with a fine mist water spray, not only feels nice on the skin, it also re-sets your foundation so that it looks fresh and natural again.

- *Make-up refresher 2* In a similar way, you don't always need to pile on more make-up under your eyes to fix where it might have settled into any creases. A tiny dab of moisturizer gently blended (use the middle finger tapping motion as explained in the 'clever concealer' section, page 124) can refresh the whole area without needing to reapply.

- *Fake beauty spot* Deal with a last minute spot crisis by forgetting about concealing it – take a brown or black eyeliner pencil and turn it into a beauty spot for the day. Set it with a dab of face powder so that it stays put all day.

- *Toning down redness* If you have a naturally ruddy complexion, if you suffer from rosacea, or if your skin has gone a bit splotchy red from being out in the cold, you can counteract the appearance of the redness by wearing a touch of a warm-toned bronzer or a peachy blusher.

- *Face shaping* By using shading and highlighting techniques, you can manipulate how the light falls on the face to give the illusion that it is either more or less defined. Remember that anywhere that you shade will recede, anywhere that you highlight will come forward. I use these techniques at work to structure noses and chins, and in photographs, it can look amazing. For day-to-day make-up though, it's best not to go too heavy. Just stick with the basics and don't get too carried away. Some basic starter points:

  - To add more definition to a round face use either a matt or a not too shimmery bronzer to shade under the cheekbones, blending all the way down past the jaw, and the temples, blending out into the hairline. Highlight the C shape around the eye as detailed in the 'how to highlight' section. Apply your blusher underneath and following the line of your cheekbone from the apple up to the hairline.

- To soften a square face use either a matt or a not too shimmery bronzer to shade the temples, blending up into the hairline, and the edges of the jaw line, and then blending out and under the ears. Highlight the C shape around the eye as detailed in the 'how to highlight' section (page 139). Apply your blusher to the apples of the cheek and blend outwards and upwards towards the hairline. Then blend either a dab of highlighter of a shimmery blusher right in the middle of the apple of the cheeks.
- To slim a wide face, apply your blusher higher up on your cheekbones and only apply highlighter to the top of the cheekbone and above the brow bone, don't join them up.

- *Defining a puffy eyelid, or one that has only a minimal socket* The eyes sometimes also need a helping hand from a bit of shade and highlight. The most common fixes have already been mentioned, but here's one that is a bit more 'pro':
  - Use a neutral shading colour like a taupe or a light brown, to add definition to the socket, extending the colour slightly higher to lift and deepen it.
  - Apply a pale shimmer shadow to the lid and under the brow, to lift these areas up.
  - Define the centre of the upper lash line with an eyeliner pencil by either dotting between the lashes or drawing a fine line close to them, and then smudging this line with either a finger or a cotton bud – make sure that it is blended outwards as well as upwards. This creates a contrast that makes the lids seem larger and the socket deeper.

- *Distraction techniques* Shading and highlighting isn't always the best solution. Sometimes you really do just end up with what looks like a dirty mark on your face. Sometimes distraction is the key: draw attention away from your nose or your round face by playing up your eyes with some eyeliner or a smoky look, or by wearing a really bold, bright lip colour.

- *Handling make-up pencils* If you can't seem to get the hang of it, try holding pencils closer to the tip for more control.

- *Stopping dark shadow from falling onto the face* Before you apply any dark coloured, powder eye shadow to the eye, look up, place a tissue under your lower lashes, as close to the lash line as you can, and hold it there. Close the eye and then apply the colour. Any stray bits of eye shadow that fall, while you are applying or blending, will be caught by the tissue and when you take it away, your face will be perfectly clean (so long as the tissue was close enough to the lash line).

- *Stopping dark shadow alternative method* If the tissue method is too fiddly, try dabbing a layer of face powder under the eye before you apply your dark eye shadow. Don't blend it in at all. Then, any shadow that falls will sit on top of this layer and disappear when you brush the powder away. I would only use this method if I were doing quite a polished, full make-up on the face, as all that powder under the eye might be more difficult to blend away if the base is really fresh and natural. Also, avoid if you have later stage skin as the powder will highlight any lines that you might have under your eyes.

- *Creating a 'cat eye'* This is the real glamour-girl look, and it is basically an alternative way to do the eyeliner definition (as detailed in the instructions for the 15-minute 'smoky eye' look (page 184):
  - Using a black or dark eyeliner pencil, rim the lower lashes at the lash line and smudge with a cotton bud.
  - Put your index finger on the outer corner of your upper lashes and pull up gently. This makes a firmer surface to draw on, and means that you just have to draw straight. Extend the line as far out as you like.
  - Make sure that the upper and lower lines meet at the outer corner of the eye before smudging the top of the upper line with a cotton bud.
  - Follow all the other shading and definition instructions as for the 'smoky eye' look (page 182), just remembering to follow the line of this new, extended eyeliner.

- *Lipliner base* There is one time when you can use lipliner before you apply lipstick or lip gloss, and that is if you want to use your lip liner as a sort of 'primer'. If you use the pencil to literally 'colour in' your whole lip (don't go over the edges!), anything that you apply on top will stay for much longer. This is especially good if you are going to a drinks party because your lipstick or gloss will usually start to come off quite quickly onto your cocktail glass, but with your pencil 'base' underneath, your lips will still look 'done'.

- *Brightening teeth* Warm-toned lipsticks will emphasize any yellow in your teeth. To make them appear brighter, stick with cool-toned lipsticks.

- *Fixing flaky nails* Switch to a stone/glass nail file. I have never looked back since I stopped using a paper file on my nails. The stone/glass files deposit tiny particles as they file the nail, this closes any gaps and stops water from being able to penetrate into the nail and cause flakiness.

- *Using make-up to look younger* Start by not wearing too much. Make-up that makes you look younger is not about covering up what you've got, it's about enhancing it and making it look its best. Create healthy, youthful, glowing skin with a combination of regular exfoliating and moisturizer. Then use a lightweight sheer base to even out the skin tone, a rosy pink cream blush blended into the apples of the cheeks and a lip colour that isn't too dark. Softly define the eyes. Go for dark tones around the eyes, but avoid black as it can be too harsh.

- *Instant no-make-up make-up* If you feel and look a bit washed-out, do a headstand against a wall, or a shoulder stand. The surge of blood that the face gets gives you an instant healthy glow. Then apply some moisturizer – as it sinks into the skin, it plumps it up and gives it an immediate radiance.

- *Bed time* One of the worst things that you can do is go to bed with your make-up on, but if you can't deal with sleeping bare-faced then exfoliate, cleanse, tone and moisturize, so that all the dirt and make-up from the day is gone. Then liven up your face with a subtle dab of a lip/cheek stain or gel – something that won't come off on the pillow, (but will still brighten your face and let you feel less 'naked').

Hair tips and tricks

- *For easy waves* Before you have your bath or shower, wrap one-inch sections of hair into pin curls and secure. Then put on a plastic shower cap and have your bath or shower. The steam and the heat can help to set the hair. Leave the shower cap on until the last minute, then whip it off, unpin your curls and shake them out loosely with your fingers. Mist with hairspray to hold.

- *For easy waves: alternative method* Loosely plait your hair before going to sleep. When you wake up in the morning, the roots will still be straight, but you will have soft waves at the tips.

- *Deep conditioning* It is really good to get into the habit of giving your hair deep conditioning treatments. The extra moisture makes hair softer and more manageable. Think of your hair as an extension of your skin. It needs moisturizing with conditioner every time you wash it and once a week a deep-conditioning mask will give it a boost of nourishment and moisture.

Top Tip: Give yourself a salon style deep-conditioning treatment at home. Apply your deep-conditioning treatment to damp hair then either wrap your hair up with plastic wrap or put on a shower cap. Then wrap a heated towel around your head and leave it on for as long as the instructions recommend. The heat will help the conditioner to penetrate deeper into the hair.

- *Dealing with frizzy curls* Either spritz with a water spray or scrunch sections with a damp flannel, then finger through a tiny amount a curl enhancer and wrap inch-sized sections of hair around a finger, slide the finger out and let the soft curls dry naturally.
- *Hair food* Just like the body, our hair responds to what we eat. Protein-rich foods and antioxidants will boost the health of your hair and essential fatty acids are great for boosting moisture levels.

Skin-care tips and tricks

- *For puffy under-eye bags* This make-up artist trick should only be used in extreme emergencies as it doesn't actually do much 'care', but it does, temporarily at least, help puffy under-eye bags to look better. Apply a thin layer of haemorrhoid cream to the puffy bit. It works by restricting the amount of fluid and contracting the blood vessels, making the area appear tighter and less puffy. I prefer to try to get rid of puffiness with a facial massage, or the tea bag trick, but if there isn't any time, and there's an event to get to or a photographer waiting, it will definitely give you a short-term solution.
- *For getting rid of blackheads* Make a paste out of a teaspoonful of baking soda and a teaspoonful of water. Massage into the skin for two to three minutes. This should loosen stubborn blackheads.
- *Home-made face mask for dry skin* Two teaspoons of milk mixed with two tablespoons of honey. Leave on for ten minutes. Rise off with warm water
- *Home-made face mask for oily skin* Finely grate one apple and mix with four tablespoons of honey. Leave on for ten minutes. Rinse off with warm water.

- *Applying face masks* Get the best out of your face mask by helping it to penetrate deeper into your skin.
  - Cleanse, exfoliate and rinse the skin clean following the instructions as detailed in the section on skin care (page 55). While cleansing, use movements from the facial massage routine in that section, to stimulate the circulation and promote the removal of toxins from the skin.
  - Soak a large flannel or a very small hand towel in some hot water (not too hot though), wring it out and hold over the face for about 30 seconds. This will open up the pores and help the mask to work deeply.
  - Pat the skin gently dry and apply your mask, avoiding the delicate eye area. Lying down flat on your back helps to continue the lymphatic drainage that you started with the massage. It also means that you can relax for a few minutes and take some time for yourself (also part of our beauty recipe). The mask can be removed either by rinsing or by gently wiping it off with a hot wet flannel or towel.
  - Finish with a spritz or wipe of toner and a layer of moisturizer as instructed in the section on skin care (page 55).
- *On Flights* Stop your skin from drying out from the low humidity by drinking lots of water, avoiding alcohol, fizzy or caffeinated drinks. Don't wear make-up and spritz your face regularly with either a water spray or a mild toner and lock the moisture in with a rich moisturizer that will act as a barrier to keep as much moisture locked into the skin as possible.

Photograph tips and tricks

Different kinds of light can affect the way you look in a photo, and there are a number of ways you can pose to make yourself look your best.

Daylight

This light is usually soft, pretty and flattering in a photo as long as you remember that between 11 a.m. and 1 p.m., the sun is overhead, and any kind of overhead lighting casts really ugly shadows under the eyes. If you have to be photographed in this light, my favourite trick was always to tilt my head to one side slightly and raise my chin up toward the light. If you smile as well, it looks natural and you get a more even and flattering light on your face. If you are allowed to choose when to have your photograph taken, the prettiest light is before the sun starts to set.

Artificial light

- When I am shooting in studios, I always use an oil control lotion before I apply foundation because shine gets magnified in photos – sometimes you can't even see it in the daylight, and using an oil control lotion beforehand saves you having to apply loads of powder.

- Remember not to put too much light-reflecting concealer under your eyes if you are going to be photographed using a flash – you don't want to have weird white stripes under your eyes in your photos.

- Photographs shot using artificial light can sometimes really drain the colour from the face. Make-up that looks fine in reality can sometimes almost disappear in pictures. Be prepared to add a little more blusher and to define the eyes a bit more heavily if necessary.

- Beware of being lit from the side, it is the make-up artist's nightmare. It might look moody and interesting, but it doesn't matter how well you have concealed any blemishes or imperfections on the face, if you then stand in light that is coming from the side, every last one will show up.

Posing

- A smile always looks good, so long as it looks natural. Instead of trying to smile with your mouth. Smile with your eyes by thinking of something that make you happy, the facial expression should then follow naturally.

> Top Tip: Beware! A smile + dark lipstick = thin lips. So go for a paler, more glossy lip.

- A relaxed mouth looks much better than a stiff rigid one. The best way to relax your mouth is to stretch it as if you were doing a massive yawn and then just let it fall back to its natural position.

- Keeping your chin up and your face turned towards the source of light (whether it is the sun, or a lamp) will always be the most flattering for your face: it stops you from having a double chin, it washes out imperfections and it can prevent the shadows that you get under your eyes when light comes from above.

- To make your body look good in a full length photo, stand sideways on from the camera, put the heel of the foot closest to the camera against the middle of the other foot, making a T shape, and slightly bend that knee. Don't let the body bend forward, keep the back straight and then twist the shoulders back towards the camera, keeping your shoulders back and your chest out. Practise in front of a full-length mirror so that you can see how it slims the waist and broadens the shoulders.

General tips and tricks

- *When working out* Save your favourite exercises till the end of your routine – to ensure that you still do them. If the end of your routine has exercises that you don't enjoy doing at all, you are much more likely to just leave them out and hit the showers!
- *At a party* Avoid getting too drunk too quickly by making your first drink a non-alcoholic, but not too sugary, one. Then when you have alcohol later, you will sip it more slowly because your thirst has already been quenched.

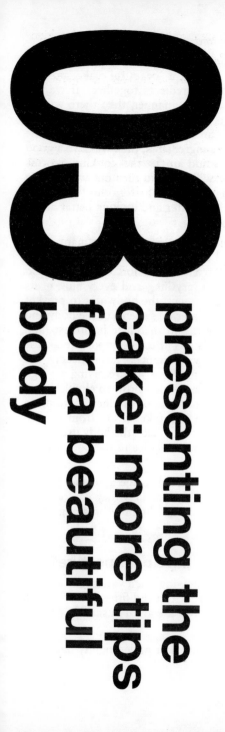

03

presenting the cake: more tips for a beautiful body

In this chapter you will learn:
- how important correct posture is
- how yoga can tone the body and relax the mind
- how to tone your body using an integrated fitness routine

Posture *(both standing and sitting)*

In the context of how I am looking at beauty, i.e. balancing the ingredients of our life and baking a 'beautiful' cake, posture would be 'how we put those ingredients together'. If we put them together in a sloppy, careless manner, then there will be lumps and holes and all sorts of things wrong with our cake. If we put our cake together carefully, taking into account the weight, size and texture of the ingredients, then we have a good chance that the cake will stand up to the cooking process without falling apart, that it will rise and turn out well. In the same way, a body with good posture can better resist the stresses and strains of life, while feeling better and looking better at the same time.

Incorrect posture can seriously affect our health in many more ways than most of us would think. This is because the human body is meant to function from a position of balance and equilibrium, with a place for everything and everything in its place. When it is in proper alignment, the body acts to prevent damage to the more vulnerable internal systems of the body and allows it to function at its best, and therefore healthiest (and most beautiful). Breathing is also as affected by posture as it is by muscular activity. When we cannot breathe deeply the muscles cannot relax because they are not receiving enough oxygen. The muscles also constrict blood flow, so circulation is affected as well. This can give a feeling of tiredness, leading to toxin build-up and ill health, which takes away from beauty. Just like the ingredients for the beauty cake, the body itself must be in balance to function properly. Balance in the body can be found through correct posture.

For most of us, incorrect posture has become a normal part of our lives and our bodies deal with it as best they can, and we don't even realize that they are almost literally breaking down under the strain.

How do you know if you have poor posture?

If you suffer from any of the following, then you might want to check your posture (see your GP, health and fitness professional, physiotherapist or osteopath if you are at all unsure):

- stiff neck
- shoulders either hunched forward or pulled tightly back
- restricted breathing

- tightness in the thighs, legs and ankles
- backaches
- headaches
- general muscle aches
- sciatica
- hip, knee pain or general joint pain
- arthritis
- chest pains and palpitations
- stomach problems
- eye strain
- hormone imbalances
- fatigue
- toothache.

What improving your posture can do for you

- It makes you look taller, slimmer and younger and can be an instant boost to your self-confidence.
- It allows more oxygen into the body, which not only makes everything function better, but it also makes your voice sound better.
- It reduces gravitational stress on the spine and ensures that all the joints work efficiently.
- It quietens the mind and can make you feel calmer, more relaxed and more physically and mentally stable.

> Top Tip: Your body uses less energy standing with correct posture than it would slouching in a chair!

The correct way to stand is with all the body's elements stacked directly above one another, from head to shoulders, to hips, knees and feet (see figure 3.1).

Correct standing posture

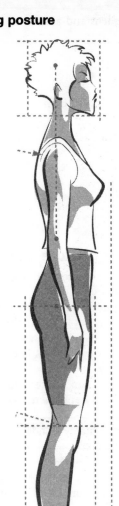

figure 3.1 correct standing posture

Incorrect standing posture

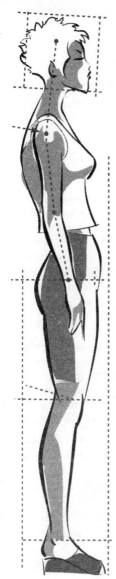

figure 3.2 incorrect standing posture

The most common problems are

- a forward head with chin jutting out
- rounded shoulders
- protruding abdomen
- excessive curve in the lower back.

How to check your standing posture

- Stand in front of a mirror and check that your alignment is correct from the front.
- Stand with your feet parallel, hip-width apart. Feel your weight on the balls, outer edges and heels of your feet. Stand so you can lift up easily through the arches.
- Soften your knees so that they are not locked.
- Put your little fingers on your hipbones and your thumbs on the bottom of your rib cage, and make sure your ribs are directly above your hips and that your pelvis is not tilted forward or backward. This is also known as 'neutral spine' and is explained further in the section on exercise (page 220).
- Lift your chest and slide your shoulder blades down and together against the back of your rib cage.
- Centre your head right on top of the spinal column.

Sitting posture

It's not just when we are standing that we need to be careful, though. The sitting position is where most of us get into trouble with poor postural habits, most often when driving or using a computer. Slouching or sitting in a slumped or awkward position for long periods of time can lead to tension and pain in both the upper and lower back and often in the neck too.

- *Head*: should be centred over shoulders about an arm length from the screen, with eyes looking straight ahead or just below horizontal.
- *Neck*: should be elongated without straining forward or backwards.
- *Shoulders*: should be comfortably held down and back.
- *Back*: should be upright while maintaining the natural curve of the lower back.
- *Elbows*: should be relaxed, close to the side of the body at about a 90 degree angle.
- *Wrists*: should be relaxed in a straight neutral position *without* resting on the wrist pad or the edge of the work-surface.

figure 3.3 correct sitting posture

figure 3.4 incorrect sitting posture

- *Fingers*: should be gently curved downwards.
- *Knees*: should be slightly lower than the hips.
- *Chair*: should be slanted slightly forward.
- *Feet*: should be planted flat on the floor.

> If we start sitting and standing correctly, our bodies will function better, we will be able to make more efficient use of our time, we will look and feel better and we will be giving the ingredients of our cake the best chance we can to work together towards our goal of maximum beauty potential.

Yoga *(including breathing and relaxation, as often as necessary)*

As we have already established, it is possible to be happier and healthier if we know and understand a little more about ourselves, our bodies and how we can improve our own health. We know that all these things work together to help us reach our beauty potential.

Understanding and using yoga can be a very effective tool in helping us to reach our goal. First let's get our facts straight:

- yoga is not just for hippies!
- you don't have to be flexible to do yoga – in fact, inflexible people can benefit the most from the physical practice of yoga
- yoga is good for our minds as well as our bodies
- regular yoga helps to improve muscle tone, flexibility, strength and stamina
- regular yoga improves posture
- yoga improves our breathing and encourages more oxygen to flow round our bodies increasing our health and vitality
- practising yoga reduces stress and tension; it calms the frenzy, clears mental clutter and allows us to get back in touch with ourselves
- yoga improves concentration, creativity, and above all a sense of well-being and calm
- even just a quick burst of yoga can settle the face and put a sparkle in the eyes.

What is yoga exactly?

Yoga can be broken down into three main parts:

- *asana* (physical postures)
- *pranayama* (breathing techniques)
- *yoga nidra* (relaxation).

The co-ordination of the *pranayama* (breath) and *asana* (physical postures) increases body awareness and develops concentration. It also promotes mental and physical health and greater self-understanding.

Asana (physical postures)

Asana practice consists of placing the body into postures, which stretch all areas of the body in a balanced way. Regular *asana* practice helps to increase muscle tone and increase flexibility – no matter what your level of flexibility and fitness may be. It also helps to improve stamina, balance, concentration and body awareness.

As with any form of exercise, if you have any illnesses or injuries, you should consult your doctor before attempting any yoga postures, and even though yoga can be extremely beneficial for pregnant women, it is best to practise with a qualified instructor. Work to your body's own limits and do not strain yourself.

A great introduction to yoga, and one of my favourite things to do in the morning to wake me up and get me energized, is the sun salutation or *surya namaskar*. Pronounced soor-yee-ah-nahma-skar, it comes from the Sanskrit *surya* meaning 'sun', and *namaskar* meaning 'salutation, greeting or praise'.

The sun salutation is a graceful sequence of 12 yoga positions performed as one continuous exercise. Practised daily it will offer greater flexibilty to your spine and joints and trim the waist. One round of sun salutation consists of two sequences, first leading with the right foot as in steps 4 and 9 (as illustrated on the following pages), the second leading with the left. Keep your hands in one place from steps 3 to 10 and try to co-ordinate your movements with your breathing. Try to do four rounds and over time you can build up to 12.

Simple sun salutation

Step one (Figure 3.5)

Stand in *mountain pose* (*tadasna*) heels and big toes touching
and correct posture (see Figure 3.1). Feel as if the upper body is
pulling in the opposite direction to your lower body. Bring the
hands together in prayer position, palm-to-palm, at the heart.

figure 3.5 step 1

Step two (Figure 3.6)

Inhale and raise the arms upward, stretching arms out to the
side and then above the head, looking at the hands.

figure 3.6 step 2

Step three (Figure 3.7)

Exhale slowly bending forward into the standing forward bend (*uttanasna*). Aim to have your hands pressed flat on the floor in line with the feet, head towards knees.

figure 3.7 step 3

Step four (Figure 3.8)

Inhale deeply and move the right leg back away from the body in a wide backward step. Keep the hands and feet firmly on the ground, with the left foot between the hands. Raise the head.

figure 3.8 step 4

Step five (Figure 3.9)

While exhaling, bring the left foot together with the right. Then press down through the palms, push the tailbone back and up, lifting the buttocks up to the sky into *downward dog* (*adho mukha svanasana*). Don't lock the elbows and keep lifting the tailbone and pressing the heels into the floor. Hold for a few breaths.

figure 3.9 step 5

Step six (Figure 3.10)

Exhale and lower the body to the floor until the feet, knees, hands, chest and forehead are touching the ground. Use your arms and try to do this in one movement.

figure 3.10 step 6

210
presenting the cake: more
tips for a beautiful body
03

Step seven (Figure 3.11)

Inhale and glide the upper body forward and between the hands into *cobra* (*bhujangasana*). Shoulders stay down and back, elbows stay tucked in and head is up. Press with the palms to open the chest even further. Don't lock the elbows or straighten the arms.

figure 3.11 step 7

Step eight (Figure 3.12)

While exhaling, tuck the toes under, then press down through the palms, push the tailbone back and up, lifting the buttocks up to the sky into *downward dog* (*adho mukha svanasana*). Don't lock the elbows and keep lifting the tailbone and pressing the heels into the floor. Hold for a few breaths.

figure 3.12 step 8

Step nine (Figure 3.13)

Inhale and bring the weight forward through the arms, lift the right foot and step it forward between the hands. Keep the hands and feet firmly on the ground. Raise the head.

figure 3.13 step 9

Step ten (Figure 3.14)

Exhale slowly bending forward into the *standing forward bend* (*uttanasna*). Aim to have your hands pressed flat on the floor in line with the feet, head towards knees.

figure 3.14 step 10

Step eleven (Figure 3.15)

Inhale and raise the arms upward, stretching arms above the head, looking at the hands.

figure 3.15 step 11

Step twelve (Figure 3.16)

Exhale and return to *mountain pose* (*tadasna*), heels and big
toes touching and correct posture. Feel as if the upper body is
pulling in the opposite direction to your lower body. Bring the
hands together in prayer position, palm-to-palm, at the heart.

figure 3.16 step 12

Repeat the whole sequence using the left leg. After you have
finished both sides you have completed one full round. Work on
making the routine fluid and on breathing evenly.

Pranayama (breathing techniques)

As mentioned before, oxygen is one of the main factors in the
formula for life. The right amount of:

> water + oxygen + nutrients = healthy cells
> = healthy body and good skin

Basic *pranayama* exercises encourage us to breathe with our
abdomen rather than our chests, this means that we use our
lungs to their full capacity, which slows down and enriches the
breathing process. Not only is oxygen intake and therefore
health and vitality increased, but this control over body and
mind encourages physical and mental relaxation. All of these
things increase our beauty potential.

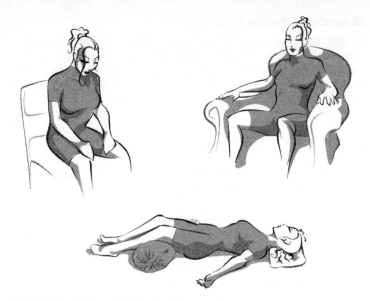

figure 3.17 suitable positions for breathing exercises

Pranayama (breathing) should always be practised in a suitable *asana* (position) – one that increases the volume of the lungs and frees the muscles of the ribs, back and diaphragm. Either sitting up straight with a neutral spine, or lying down works best (see Figure 3.17).

- If you suffer from chronic shortness of breath or other breathing disorders check with your GP first.
- Don't exhaust yourself as this defeats the purpose.
- Breathing exercises work best on an almost empty stomach.
- Don't try to hurry any of the breathing exercises. Try to keep the breath smooth and steady, otherwise the whole purpose of *pranayama* is lost.

Breath awareness exercise

Most people do not breathe properly and fully, the breath normally being shallow and focused in the upper chest. The following exercise shows us how to be aware of our breathing.

Take normal breaths for one minute. Count how many 'out breaths' you make in one minute. Practise trying to steadily slow down the pace of your inhalations and exhalations. Aim for under eight in a minute. This would indicate a good amount of oxygen entering the body and sufficient expulsion of waste.

Abdominal breathing exercise

Sit upright, place your hands gently on your lower stomach, close your eyes and gently press your tongue to the roof of your mouth. Breathe in slowly and steadily through your nose and feel the air slowly filling the bottom of your lungs. You should feel your abdomen expand slightly. Breathe out through your mouth (your tongue will automatically come away from the roof of your mouth) and be aware of your abdomen contracting. It should feel as if you are slowly and steadily blowing out a long line of candles. Repeat ten times – if you start to feel giddy, pause for about 30 seconds, then begin again. You can also do the same exercise lying down with the knees bent up.

Top Tip: This is great to do if you are really stressed out and you feel like you are about to boil over.

Nadi shodhana exercise

This is great for stress. It can also help to soothe the anxiety caused by flying or other stressful situations.

- Hold your right hand up and curl your index and middle fingers towards your palm. Place your thumb next to your right nostril. Close the left nostril by pressing gently against it with your ring finger and inhale through the right nostril. The breath should be slow, steady and full.
- Now close the right nostril by pressing gently against it with your thumb and open your left nostril by relaxing your ring finger and exhale fully with a slow and steady breath.
- Inhale though the left nostril, close it, and then exhale through the right nostril.

(That's one complete round of *nadi shodhana* – inhale through the right nostril, exhale through the left, inhale through the left, exhale through the right)

Begin with five to ten rounds and add more as you feel comfortable. Remember to keep your breathing slow and easy. Full *nadi shodhana* can be practised just about any time and anywhere. *Nadi shodhana* helps control stress and anxiety. If you start to feel stressed, ten or so rounds will help calm you down.

Yoga nidra (relaxation)

Relaxation is a fantastic antidote for stress (see the section on stress, page 41) and can even lower our blood pressure. It is great for times when we need to focus and even better for when we need to clear our heads and get a good night's sleep. Stress relief and restful sleep are both important ingredients in our recipe for beauty. So learning to relax can be a great way for us to maintain a good balance.

The corpse pose

Lie on your back, feet spread a bit wider than hip-width apart and hands about six inches (15 cms) from your sides, palms up. Ease yourself into the pose. Let your thighs, knees and toes turn outward. Close your eyes and breathe deeply.

The corpse pose, or *savasana*, is the classic relaxation pose. It looks deceptively simple, but it is in fact one of the most difficult *asanas* to do well and one that changes and develops with practice. When you first lie down, look to see that you are lying symmetrically, as symmetry provides proper space for all parts to relax. Now start to work in the pose. Rotate your legs in and out, then let them fall gently out to the sides. Do the same with your arms. Rotate the spine by turning your head from side to side to centre it. Then start stretching yourself out, as though someone were pulling your head away from your feet, your shoulders down and away from your neck, your legs down and away from your pelvis. Let gravity embrace you. Feel your weight pulling you deeper into relaxation, melting your body into the floor. Breathe deeply and slowly from the abdomen, riding up and down on the breath, sinking deeper with each exhalation. Feel how your abdomen swells and falls. Many physiological changes are taking place, reducing the body's energy loss, removing stress, lowering your respiration and pulse rate and resting the whole system. As you enter deep relaxation, you will feel your mind grow clear and detached.

Breath counting

Breathe in deeply through the nose, using all the areas of the chest. Hold for a count of five, breathe out for as long as possible through the mouth, making sure that your lungs are completely empty. Repeat three times, but count how long your out breaths are and try to extend by one each time by controlling the abdomen and concentrating. This will induce relaxation.

Note: Deep breathing can make you feel dizzy and light-headed. This is because the amount of oxygen and carbon dioxide in the body is changing and the balance between these chemicals is disturbed. If this occurs, just rest a little. After a few moments you should feel balanced again.

Relaxation exercise

During this exercise, you relax each part of the body in turn. But in order to experience relaxation, you must first experience tension. Working up from the feet, as shown below, you first tense and lift each part, then drop (but don't place) it down. Now let your mind travel throughout the body, commanding each part to relax. Let yourself go. Sink deep into the quiet pool of the mind. To bring your consciousness back to your body, gently move your fingers and toes, take a deep breath and as you exhale, sit up.

- *Feet and legs* Lift your right foot just an inch off the floor. Tense the leg, hold, then let it drop. Repeat on the other side.
- *Hands and arms* Raise your right hand an inch off the floor. Make a fist, tense the arm, then let it drop. Repeat on the other side. Relax.
- *Buttocks* Clench your buttocks tightly together, lift the hips a little way off the floor and hold. Relax and drop them down.
- *Chest* Tense and lift up the back and chest, keeping your hips and head on the floor. Relax and drop them down.
- *Shoulders* Lift your shoulders and hunch them up tight around your neck. Let them drop, relaxed. Now pull each arm, in turn, down alongside the body, and relax.
- *Head* Tuck in your chin slightly and roll the head gently from side to side. Find a comfortable position in the centre for the head to lie, and then relax.

Exercise *(one hour, three times a week)*

Regular exercise is vital for a healthy body and a healthy mind and, therefore, an important ingredient that is needed to balance our recipe for beauty.

Physical benefits

On a physical level, exercise increases the amount of oxygen that flows to all the cells in our bodies. This has many benefits:

- It allows nutrients to be absorbed more efficiently and cells to grow faster.
- It means more collagen is produced which improves the texture and moisture retention of our skin, making it more plump and youthful.
- It boosts circulation, which can improve sluggish digestion and bring an instant glow to the skin.
- More oxygen intake also means less free radical damage (see the section on free radicals, page 7).

On top of all that, regular exercise builds strong muscles and bones, which will help to prevent common age-related diseases in later life, such as osteoporosis, high blood pressure and heart disease.

Mental benefits

On a mental level, exercise releases chemicals in the brain that lift our mood if we are feeling down. The boost in circulation can give us energy if we are feeling tired. Also, regular exercise can make us more realistic about our bodies and accepting of things about ourselves that we can't actually change. This opens the door for a much more positive attitude (see the section on self-esteem, page 258).

I asked my personal trainer, Henry Abrahams, to help me put together a plan that could be modified to suit anyone who wanted to use exercise as a way to not only boost their health and fitness, but also as part of their recipe for beauty. He says that:

> 'An integrated fitness programme is the most effective way to maintain good fitness, muscle tone and weight loss. This involves "cross training", which means using your time to do a variety of different types of exercise including cardiovascular, resistance, core stability and flexibility training. This gets the best results because it increases total calorific expenditure and boosts metabolism for longer, post exercise.'

- *Cardiovascular training* is anything that increases the heart rate. It includes things like running, cycling, rowing, dancing, stepping, skipping or training on the elliptical trainer (also known as the 'cross training' machine – not to be confused with a 'cross training' programme). Cardiovascular training at 80 per cent of your maximum heart rate can increase your resting metabolic rate (the rate at which your body burns calories when you are sitting still) by as much as 13 per cent after ten weeks of training. (Check with your health and fitness professional to find out how to work this out.)
- *Core stability training* focuses on creating a firm and strong stomach, which in turn supports the spine and improves posture (see core stability exercises).
- *Resistance training* increases muscle strength, muscle endurance and muscle power and should not be confused with weightlifting, power-lifting or bodybuilding (see resistance training exercises).
- *Flexibilty training* (stretching) can improve posture and help to prevent lower back pain. Regular stretching promotes relaxation in the tissues and is important for maintaining healthy joints (see flexibility training exercises).

The full programme

In an ideal situation, we would have one hour, three times a week, to do a routine like this:

- 10 mins warm-up: gentle cardiovascular training followed by three or more flexibility exercises – focus on hip flexors, calves and lats
- 10 mins of cardiovascular interval training (slower pace for a certain time followed by a fast pace for a certain time – 30 secs + 30 secs, 1 min + 1 min, whatever suits you best)
- 10 mins of core stability training
- 10 mins cardio vascular interval training (preferably a different type to the last time)
- 10 mins of resistance training
- 10 mins cool-down: very gentle cardio vascular training (walking or swimming) and some more stretching (at least three).

You can do this routine at home, or at the gym. If you are doing these exercises at the gym, then you can use the hand weights – speak to one of the health and fitness professionals at your gym to find out which weights are best for you to use. If you are doing them at home, a couple of small bottles of water or tins of beans (whatever you can easily hold in your hands) should give you enough resistance. If you can't spare an hour, three times a week, then try to do the 'bite-sized' version (at the end of this section, page 236) as often as you can.

If you do the core and resistance training exercises 'circuit-style', i.e. one complete set of every exercise, before going back to do subsequent sets, you will get the most benefit from them. Two to three circuits is recommended.

Top Tip: It is useful to do all of the following exercises in front of a mirror so that you can constantly check that you are maintaining good posture (and therefore gaining the most from the exercise and also protecting your body from any injuries – two steps towards a better beauty cake!).

Remember that if you have any sort of illness or health concern, you should always consult with your GP before beginning any exercise program.

Core stability exercises

Neutral spine

In all exercises you need to have correct posture, which involves having a 'neutral spine'. To find your neutral spine position, lie on the floor with your knees bent up and your feet hip width apart and flat on the floor. Neutral spine is the position that lies between the pelvis being tucked under and the spine being arched (do both so that you can feel the difference). In neutral spine, the length of the spine is elongated, but you could still pass an envelope under your lower back. Recognize how this feels and then translate it into sitting and standing positions as well.

Engage the abdominals

In all of the exercises, you have to 'engage your abdominals'. Think of sucking your belly button towards your spine and keeping it locked in that position. In this position it's like having a girdle of strength around your middle – your spine is protected and you will find that it feels like you have extra power.

Practise having a neutral spine and then engaging the abdominals without disrupting the neutral spine. By exercising in this position the body will gain the maximum benefit.

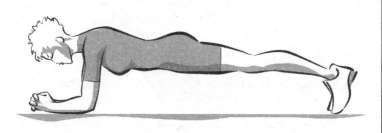

figure 3.18 the plank

Top Tip: If you ever feel like you are flagging and you want to give up, concentrate on engaging the abdominals even more and you may find that you are able to finish the exercise more easily.

The plank

Aim to hold this position for 20 seconds, gradually building to one minute.

Lie face down on the floor, stretching yourself out as long as possible. Clasp your hands together and, with your elbows directly beneath your shoulders, slowly raise your body up until just your elbows, your lower arms and toes touch the floor and the rest of your body is held in a straight line parallel with the floor (Figure 3.18). Engage your abdominals and use them to hold you straight and stop yourself from sagging in the middle.

Easy version: feet together
Advanced version: feet hip-width apart.

Note: if you start to feel pressure on your lower back, it may be because your spine is not in neutral. Engage your abdominals and find neutral spine again and the pressure should be relieved.

Crunches (avoid this exercise if you have any neck problems)

figure 3.19 crunch start

figure 3.20 crunch finish

Start with 15 to 20, building up to 30.

Lie on the floor, knees bent, feet hip-width apart and flat on the floor and spine in neutral. Place the hands lightly by the sides of the ears, elbows out to the side. Curl your shoulders forward keeping the lower back on the floor (Figure 3.19). Take a breath in, then, as you breathe out, engage the abdominals and lift your shoulders up, curling in towards your belly button (Figure 3.20). Imagine that you have a tennis ball under your neck and this will keep your neck in line with the spine and keep the elbows out wide to stop the upper body from scrunching up. Also, in order to end up with a really flat tummy, try not to let your stomach 'pop up' – try to keep it as flat as possible the whole way through the exercise, and don't be tempted to tuck in the pelvis – concentrate on keeping the neutral spine position.

Oblique crunches (avoid this exercise if you have any neck problems)

figure 3.21 oblique crunches

Start with 10, build up to 20.

Lie on the floor, legs straight, feet hip-width apart and spine in neutral. Place the hands lightly by the sides of the ears, elbows out to the side. Take a breath in, then breathe out, engage the abdominals, keep the neck relaxed and bend and lift your right leg while moving your left elbow to meet it (Figure 3.21). Breathe in and lower back down again. Repeat the whole sequence using the opposite arm and leg. The elbows need to stay wide to ensure that the shoulder has to lift off the floor each time. As above, imagine that you have a tennis ball under your neck, concentrate on keeping a neutral spine and flattened abdominals.

Resistance training exercises

Lots of women are put off the idea of doing resistance training because it involves weights and they think that it means that they will build big muscles if they do it. If you are using the appropriate weights for your strength and build, resistance training will tone the body, building lean muscle (which burns more calories at rest), improve posture and help to prevent health problems like osteoperosis later in life. If you are unsure about how much weight is appropriate for you, check with one of the health and fitness professionals at your local gym.

> Top Tip: As a general rule, you breathe out on contraction (when the muscles have to do the hard work).

Tricep dips (get rid of bingo wings)

Do 15–20 repetitions.

Start with your back close to a bench or chair with your hands over its arm/edge and your feet about three to four feet (1 metre) away and with a neutral spine (Figure 3.22). Breathe in, engage the abdominals and lower your body so that your elbows are bent at 90 degrees with your back remaining close to the chair/bench (Figure 3.23). Breathe out as you push back up again. Try not to 'sit' into the movement, make sure that all the work is being done by your arms.

figure 3.22 tricep dip start   **figure 3.23** tricep dip finish

Lateral raises (for toning shoulders)

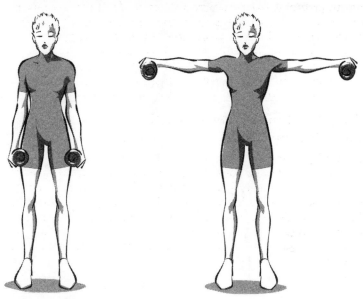

figure 3.24 lateral raises

Do 15–20 repetitions.

Stand with your feet hip-width apart, knees slightly bent and with a neutral spine. Holding hand weights by your sides with palms facing inwards, engage your abdominals and breathe in, then breathe out as you slowly lift your arms away from your sides, keeping elbows slightly bent until your hands are at shoulder height (Figure 3.24). Keep palms facing down and do not allow your hands to twist. Breathe in as you lower again. Aim to keep the whole upper body as still as possible.

Single arm shoulder press (for sculpting shoulders and upper arms)

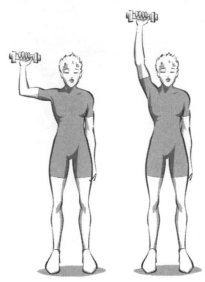

figure 3.25 shoulder press

Do 15–20 repetitions for each arm.

Stand with your feet hip-width apart, knees slightly bent and neutral spine. Holding a hand weight in one hand, bend that arm up to 90 degrees with your elbow at shoulder level. Engage the abdominals and breathe in. As you breathe out push the weight up so that it is above your head (Figure 3.25). Breathe in as you lower again. Aim to keep the whole upper body as still as possible, especially the other shoulder.

Easy version: single arm press (as shown)

Advanced version: double arm press. As single arm press, but with both arms at the same time – make sure to keep spine in neutral and the abdominals engaged the whole time to avoid any strain on the lower back. The advanced version also saves a bit of time.

Bicep curls (for sleek arms)

figure 3.26 bicep curls

Do 15–20 repetitions.

Stand with your feet hip-width apart, knees slightly bent and with a neutral spine. Holding hand weights by your sides with your elbows slightly bent and your palms facing outwards. Engage your abdominal muscles and breathe in. As you breathe out, bend your arms and lift the weights towards your shoulders (Figure 3.26). Breathe in as you lower your arms down again. Keep your elbows tucked into your waist and keep the movement slow and controlled. Don't be tempted to jerk or use your body to give you momentum – try to keep the whole upper body as still as possible.

Static lunges (sexy legs and a pert bottom)

figure 3.27 static lunges

Do ten on each leg.

Stand up straight, neutral spine, breathe in and engage the abdominals. As you breathe out, take a large stride forward and lower the body into a lunge position with your back knee lowering towards the floor. Make sure that the front knee doesn't go over the front of your foot. Breathe in and return to the standing position. Keeping the abdominals engaged, repeat with the other leg (Figure 3.27). Keep the back straight the whole time.

Leg raises (to lift the bottom)

Do 25–30 each side.

Start on your hands and knees on the floor (with your arms a shoulder-width apart and knees hip-width apart). Then lower yourself so that your elbows support you, you can clasp hands if it is more comfortable. Straighten one leg out behind so that only the toes are touching the floor (Figure 3.28). Check that you have a neutral spine, then engage your abdominals and use the muscles in your bottom (your 'glutes') to slowly raise the straightened leg up off the floor until it is in a straight line with your shoulders. Don't lift it higher than this as it can put pressure on the lower back. Keeping the abdominals engaged, lower the leg back down until the toes are touching the floor again. Like in the 'plank' exercise, it is very important to keep the spine neutral and to use your stomach muscles to hold you straight and stop yourself from sagging in the middle and therefore putting pressure on the lower back. Breathe naturally, making sure that you don't hold your breath.

figure 3.28 leg raises

Flexibility exercises

Stretching properly helps reduce risk of injury as well as minimizing post work-out aches and pains. Stretch to the point of tension – not pain, hold for at least 20 seconds and then slowly release. Don't be tempted to bounce because it is counterproductive. Muscles have a reflex to protect them against stretching too fast or too far and bouncing can trigger this response and cause them to tighten instead of relaxing and stretching. If you want to increase the stretch, move a tiny bit deeper into the stretch on each breath out.

Hip flexor stretch

Kneel on the floor with one knee out in front and the back leg extended slightly as shown. Tilt the pelvis forward and under until a stretch is felt at the top of the leg. Try not to lean forward or bend the front leg more than 90 degrees. Don't lean on the hands too much, just use them for support. Once you are confident, you can do this exercise with your hands on your hips. Repeat with the other knee up.

figure 3.29 hip flexor stretch

Calf stretch

figure 3.30 calf stretch

Standing three to four feet (1 metre) from wall with feet in the position shown, with toes pointing towards the wall, lean against the forearms while trying to maintain a straight line through the spine and keeping the back heel pressed into the ground and feet facing forward. Repeat on the other leg.

Lat and tricep stretch

figure 3.31 lat and tricep stretch

Reach one hand up and behind the head as if you are going to scratch your back. Hold the raised elbow with the other hand and pull on it so that the hand moves farther down your back and you feel the stretch in your upper arm. Repeat on the other side.

Hamstring stretch

Lie flat on the floor with the knees bent and feet hip-width apart and flat on the floor. Then slowly raise and straighten one leg, grasping it loosely behind the thigh with both hands. Keep straightening it until you feel the stretch in your hamstring. If you are very flexible, keep it straight and gently pull the leg towards you. Keep the pelvis on the floor. Repeat with the other leg.

figure 3.32 hamstring stretch

Standing quadriceps stretch

figure 3.33 standing quadriceps stretch

Stand with one hand on a wall for balance. Bring the foot up to your hand and grasp the ankle. Gently pull up until the stretch is felt. Keep your knees pressed together. Turn to face the opposite direction and repeat on the other leg.

Chest stretch

figure 3.34 chest stretch

Stand in a doorway and place feet facing forwards and bend your arm as shown. Slowly lean forward until a stretch is felt in the chest region. Repeat on the other side. If you can reach you can do both sides at the same time.

Shoulder stretch

Reach one arm across your body and hold it straight. Use the other arm to grasp the elbow and pull it across the body towards the chest. You should feel the stretch in the back of the shoulder. Repeat on the other side.

figure 3.35 shoulder stretch

Lower back stretch

figure 3.36 lower back stretch

Lie on your back with your knees bent up. Slowly pull the knees to the chest until you feel a gentle stretch in the lower back.

Top Tip: A stability ball can be used to do not only these, but also a wide range of stretches, core and resistance exercises. Speak to your local health and fitness professional if you are interested in finding out more.

Bite-sized version

- 5 mins cardiovascular activity of your choice – (doubles as warm-up)
- 1 min core – the plank (three sets of 20 secs)
- 2 mins resistance – combine bicep curls, double arm shoulder raises and static lunges into one exercise, as follows:
  - Stand up straight holding hand weights by your sides with your elbows slightly bent and your palms facing outwards.
  - Check that you have a neutral spine, engage the abdominals and take a large stride forward and lower the body into a lunge position with your back knee lowering towards the floor. Make sure that the front knee doesn't go over the front of your foot.
  - Bend your arms and lift the weights towards your shoulders, then push the weights up so that they are above your head.
  - Still in the lunge position, lower the arms back to the shoulders, then, keeping your elbows tucked into your waist, lower them all the way back down to your sides.
  - Keep the movement slow and controlled and don't be tempted to jerk or use your body to give you momentum – try to keep the whole upper body as still as possible.
  - Return to the standing position and repeat on the other leg.
  - Keep the abdominals engaged and a neutral spine throughout. Breathe naturally and don't hold your breath.
  - Try for ten on each side.
- 2 mins flexibility – hip flexors, calves and lats.

This is ten minutes. If you can spare another couple of minutes then add in something else – if you want to work more on your arms add in some tricep dips, or if you want to work your bottom add some leg raises. Obviously, to get the best results, the best thing to do is the full programme three times a week (you could do it seven times a week if you had the time and inclination – you will see results much faster), but this is a way to make really good use of a spare ten minutes and most people can find a spare ten minutes each day.

Alternatively, there is a wide selection of videos available for use at with at home. I am particularly partial to the high-energy dance style ones, I always feel like I have had a really good workout afterwards.

Failing all that, here are some tips that you can integrate into your daily life to increase the amount of exercise you get:

- Walk up or down escalators.
- Take the stairs instead of the lift/elevator.
- Don't fight for the parking space that is nearest to where you need to be, park a bit further away and walk.
- Use a tube or bus stop that is further away than the one which you usually use (either at the beginning or end of your journey) and walk the rest.
- If you have a supermarket within walking distance and you can find the time, don't take the car and do a weekly shop, go every couple of days and walk there and back. Only shopping for a couple of days will mean that the bags will be manageable.
- While using the telephone at home, walk around at the same time (not advisable at work!).

237
presenting the cake: more
tips for a beautiful body
03

04

a cake for all occasions: every body can be beautiful

In this chapter you will learn:

- about male grooming
- about beauty and pregnancy
- about beauty and long-term illness

Male grooming

Personally I'm not the biggest fan of men wearing make-up, unless you are a rock star or in fancy dress. When I have groomed male celebrities like Donald Sutherland, Bill Nighy and Goran Visnijc I have tended to stick with a basic 'de-shine and de-blemish' routine as opposed to full-on 'newsreader'-style make-up. I do, however, wholeheartedly support the idea of men looking after their skin and making a bit of an effort with their appearance. So, for the man who isn't embarrassed to say that he takes care of himself, first let me say 'Well done!' and second let me provide you with some of the basic things that you might want to know about the world of male grooming. Please take it on board and use it to your advantage.

Skin care

Men's skin is not that different from women's skin (for more information, please refer to the section on skin care, page 55). The epidermis is slightly thicker, the facial hair is thicker and stronger and the sebaceous glands produce more sebum. The skin needs to be cleansed regularly to stop this sebum (oil) from building up and blocking the pores on the face and causing spots and blackheads. Also, to keep the skin supple and younger-looking, it is important to exfoliate twice a week and moisturize every day after cleansing. It is also just as important for men as it is for women to know that the health of their skin is directly related to the health of their body and that living a healthy and balanced life vastly improves the appearance of the skin. Chapters 1 and 3 describe all these factors in much more detail.

Skin-care routine

- *Cleanse* The easiest and most beneficial way to clean your face is to use a soap-free face wash or facial cleansing bar. These are better for the skin than soap, which can dry the skin out and upset its natural pH balance. Massage a small amount into damp skin to get a good lather, then rinse off thoroughly. This is quick and easy to do while in the shower. If you are using the sink, use warm running water to rinse off.
- *Exfoliate* Exfoliating twice a week helps to prevent in-grown hairs while at the same time brightening up dull and tired-looking skin by sloughing off the outer layer of dead skin cells. The easiest way to exfoliate is to use a face scrub. It is like a face wash, but has little grains in it. Massage into the skin and rinse off in the same way. Don't scrub too hard, think 'polish' rather than 'scour'.

- *Tone* Splashing the face lightly with cool (but not icy cold) water, closes all the now clean pores, and gives the face a damp surface on which to apply your moisturizer. Applying moisturizer to a damp face locks as much moisture as possible into the skin to keep it fresh and healthy looking. It also means that you don't have to use quite so much.

- *Moisturize* Oil-free moisturizers are good for most men, even if the skin feels dry. The dryness is usually a result of dehydration, not lack of oil. Increase your water level by drinking at least two litres of water a day and boosting your intake of high water content fruits and vegetables. For more information on water, please refer to the section on hydration (page 19). If looking older is a concern, then start using a moisturizer that also contains sun protection, since the sun is responsible for 80 per cent of the skin's ageing.

Dealing with skin-care problems

- *Shiny skin* If your skin is very oily, you may want to use an oil-control moisturizer instead of an oil-free one. These moisturize the skin while at the same time 'mopping up' any excess shine. You could also apply a mattifying lotion over your moisturizer to keep any shine at bay throughout the day. This is what I use instead of powder when I am grooming male celebrities as it soaks up ugly shine without looking like there is anything on the face.

- *Spots* Don't squeeze them. Stick with the skin-care routine, and apply a spot treatment (something with salicylic acid, benzoyl peroxide or tea tree oil) to encourage the spot to heal faster. There is more detailed information about spots in the 'banishing blemishes' section (page 90).

- *Sensitive skin* If your skin goes red and blotchy or certain products sting, you may have sensitive skin. Avoid using any products that have too many chemicals in them, watch out for things with alcohol or fragrance (especially aftershave) and make sure that you wear sun protection when outside as sensitive skins are more likely to burn in the sun. Stick to using gentle shaving products: shave oil tends to be the kindest to the skin.

Shaving

Having a good skin-care routine can make shaving a little bit easier. Regular cleansing and exfoliation keeps the skin clean and the beard soft and therefore easier to remove.

Wet shave

A wet shave is the best way to get a close shave, but it isn't as quick and simple as shaving with an electric razor. This guide is designed to help you get the best shave possible.

- Don't shave the minute you wake up in the morning. The face needs about 20 minutes for its muscles to tighten and settle properly.

- Make sure your razor is really sharp, and that your face is clean.

- If the pores on the face are open before you start, you will get a smoother, cleaner shave. Either shave directly after your shower, or hold a flannel soaked in hot water over your face for about 30 seconds first.

- Dampen the skin and apply your shaving medium, massaging it well into the area to be shaved. Oils or cream give the best results and are a lot less drying and irritating than foams, gels or the traditional soap and brush.

- To get the closest shave you need, stretch the skin that you are shaving. Do this by either by puffing out your cheek, tensing the muscles or pulling slightly with your fingers.

- Use short strokes to shave in the same direction as the hair growth. This helps to avoid rashes and in-grown hairs. You can shave in both directions on the neck, though.

- Ease up on the pressure on high areas such as the jaw line and try to always keep the angle of the blade the same. This helps to avoid nicks.

- Don't tip your head over to one side at an angle to shave your sideburns, as it is really difficult to see if they are even. Try keeping your head straight up and simply turn it and look to the side.

- Use *hot* and preferably running water (for hygiene reasons) to rinse your razor, especially if you are using shaving oil. Cold water won't dissolve it.

- When you are finished, rinse any residue off the face with warm water and then splash with cool water. This closes the pores and refreshes the skin.

- If you have any areas that feel irritated, apply an aftershave balm, and then a moisturizer, to the rest of your face. Otherwise, apply moisturizer all over the face and neck.

Top Tip: If you cut yourself, the best way to stop the bleeding is to dab it with a styptic pencil (available from most chemists). This will stop the flow of blood and disinfect the skin.

Electric

Using an electric razor will be much quicker and less messy, but can sometimes be harsh on the skin and can pull the hair.

- To make an electric shave go a bit smoother, try using a pre-shave lotion to soften the hair first.
- Now pull the skin gently with one hand and with the other hand use gentle pressure to shave against the grain of your beard growth – this will give you the closet shave.
- Don't press down too hard, or move your shaver too rapidly over your face. It won't give you a closer shave, all it will do is wear out your razor faster.

Top Tip: If your skin is sensitive it can help to shave the most tender areas of your face (the neck area below the jawbone) first before the razor gets hot.

Beware of aftershaves as they can really dry the skin out. They have a very high alcohol content and alcohol dehydrates the skin. When the skin is too dry, it can start to overproduce oil, which can lead to problems like blackheads and spots.

Dealing with shaving problems

Shaving rash

A shaving rash is usually the result of too much friction as your razor moves over your skin. Reasons for this could be:

- a shaving medium that is too harsh – gels and foams can be quite drying, try switching to something like an oil or a cream that would provide more lubrication
- the hairs are too dry and hard when they are shaved – soften the bristles by making sure that the face is warm and wet before you start
- a razor that isn't sharp enough – change your blades regularly for a smoother shave
- if none of those options seem to help, you may have sensitive skin, in which case you need to use a mild and gentle shave medium that is specially formulated for sensitive skin.

Applying a soothing shave balm afterwards will help to calm any irritation.

Ingrown hairs

- Ingrown hairs can be an unfortunate result of regular shaving, but if the shaving guide above is followed, the chances of getting them are minimized. Also, a good skin-care routine that includes regular exfoliation and moisturizing to keep the skin clear and soft, can also go a long way to preventing the chance of ingrown hairs.
- Ingrown hairs occur when a hair fails to reach the follicle opening and curls back on itself, sometimes becoming trapped under a fine layer of skin. Other times, sebum (oil) can build up around the hair and cause it to become infected and swollen and sometimes sore.
- Gentle daily exfoliation can often get rid of the 'non angry' hairs that you can see under the surface.
- Be careful picking at the more angry ones – just like with spots, you could end up with a scar. The safest way to deal with them is to apply an ingrown hair lotion that will dry up the skin and draw the offending hair to the surface where it can be easily removed with a pair of sterilized tweezers. Like spot treatments, lotions including tea-tree oil, or salycillic acid should do the trick.

Eyebrows

I asked Paul Merritt, co-Director of Bloww (a high end London salon) and former manager of Channel 4's *The Salon*, to give me some advice about men's eyebrows. He said:

'Eyebrows can often get out of control and sometimes need a bit of a helping hand to look respectable. A little trim now and again and five minutes with a pair of tweezers can really make a difference and frame the face, giving an altogether smarter and more finished look. However, if it's your first attempt, I would advise visiting a professional so as to set the boundaries for a natural look for when you have a go yourself … there's nothing worse than getting carried away and ending up with rainbow-brows!'

These tips should help if you are brave enough to try for yourself though:

- *If they are too bushy:* Tweeze away some of the underneath hairs – just a few will make enough of a difference and won't leave you looking like you've 'done' your eyebrows. Pluck out any that grow too far down your temples too, as this can make your eyes appear droopy and sad!

Tweezing technique:

- Sterilize your tweezers first by running them under the hot tap or dipping them in surgical spirit.
- Stretch the skin a little to make it easier and carefully pluck any stray hairs, one at a time, in the direction of the hair growth.
- Keep standing back from the mirror to check that you haven't overdone it.
- Like shaving, this is best done after your shower or after holding a hot flannel to your face for 30 seconds as it makes the hairs come out more easily (and is therefore less painful!)

Top Tip: Run over them a few times with an ice cube wrapped in a flannel to soothe your brows if they feel a bit tender afterwards.

- *If they are long and wiry*: Use a small sharp pair of scissors to carefully trim the offending ones one at a time. If you cut them slightly at an angle, they will look more natural.
- *If you have a mono-brow*: Use the tweezing technique mentioned above to pluck a clean gap that is about as wide as a finger to separate your brows. This will lighten up the face and make it appear less sinister.

Hair

Dealing with fine/thin hair

A good haircut can really help to give the illusion of thicker hair. Washing your hair with a thickening shampoo and conditioner can give a bit of extra volume, as can drying it with a spritz of a thickening lotion.

Dealing with products

- *Gel* Use gel for a firm hold; good for 'slicked back' styles and shine.
- *Pomade or wax* These can either hold hair in place with a more natural-looking finish than gel, or can be good for creating texture and movement in quite a styled way.
- *Creams or gums* These are similar to pomade and wax, but usually have a more matt finish. They allow you to add texture and movement to the hair in a more natural and casual-looking way.

Dealing with hair loss

Hair loss is partly genetic and partly due to a combination of hormones and the health of your scalp. There isn't much that we can do to get around the part that genes play, but scalp health and some hormonal activity is definitely controllable.

- DHT (Dihydrotestosterone) is an androgen and it is the hormone that attacks the hair follicles causing hair to then fall out. The body needs certain amounts of androgen hormones in order to function properly, but it can often over produce them as a result of stress. There is more detailed information about this in the section on stress (page 41). It follows then that lowering stress levels in your life increases the life expectancy of your hair.
- Having healthy hair is another way to build resistance to hair loss. A healthy diet is the easiest way to improve the strength of your hair. Good foods to include are: lean protein and soy products as well as beans, whole grains, fresh fruits and vegetables.
- Lastly, a healthy scalp can also help in the prevention of hair loss. Keep it clean and keep the skin from drying out and becoming weak by washing regularly and using conditioner. Conditioner is as much for the scalp as it is for the hair.

Back and chest hair

If you want to remove any back and chest hair, shaving is an option, although doing your back can be tricky and you might feel quite itchy as the stubble re-grows. Waxing is a better alternative as the hairs grow back finer and the finish stays smoother for much longer. If you are brave you can try it at home, but most beauty salons offer chest and back waxes as a regular treatment for men. For a more permanent solution, electrolysis and laser treatment can be options. There is more information about both of these in the hair removal section.

Beauty and pregnancy

When you are pregnant, people are always telling you that you are glowing and beautiful, but your internal hormonal changes can often leave you feeling just the opposite. Sometimes the bloating, weight gain, skin problems, hair problems and even teeth and gum problems can just get a bit overwhelming.

Skin

During pregnancy, skin can fluctuate between being oily and being dry. Some people develop acne and others may find that their acne clears up. While most of these changes will revert back a short while after you have given birth, it is still important to adapt your beauty routine to suit how your skin is behaving at the time (see the section on skin care, page 55).

Apart from daily cleansing and moisturizing, make sure to exfoliate once a week as this leaves skin soft and smooth, radiant and more receptive to other skin-care products, especially moisturizer. A weekly face mask is also good for pampering and can boost either hydration, radiance, firming or soothing whatever is most necessary (see the section on skin care, page 55).

Top Tip: It is important to be aware that cell turnover is accelerated during pregnancy – so make sure you nourish and moisturize more than normal to keep skin looking and feeling healthy.

It is quite common to see an increase in amounts of facial hair during pregnancy. Tweezing or bleaching are the most popular ways to deal with it, but be sure to consult with your GP before using any hair removal method that involves chemicals or drugs.

Skin is also more prone to pigmentation issues when you are pregnant and it can also tan and burn much more easily. Try to avoid too much sun exposure and if you are going on holiday make sure that you are well protected: wear a sun hat and use a good SPF, frequently applied (and don't forget hands and feet!).

The skin is extra sensitive during pregnancy, so it is important to check that your products are pregnancy suitable:

- Avoid AHAs or products containing vitamin A (retinol).
- Avoid daily use of benzoul peroxide (an acne cream) all over the face. A lot of acne creams are not suitable for use during pregnancy. If you have acne then check the suitability of your cream with your GP.
- Avoid dyeing the roots of your hair and getting chemicals on your scalp (take advice from your hairdresser).
- Avoid using hair removal creams.
- Avoid using the following essential oils: basil, clove, cinnamon, hyssop, juniper, marjoram, myrrh, sage and thyme

at any time during the pregnancy. Fennel, peppermint and rosemary should not be used during the first four months, but after that they are acceptable to use in small doses. If you are unsure check with a qualified aromatherapist.
- Avoid soap because it strips the skin of its natural oils and upsets the pH balance of the skin.

Top Tip: Don't stay too long in the bath, because it dehydrates the skin. Try to moisturize within three minutes to lock in any residual moisture.

Self and health

Nutrition is very important. Eat plenty of vitamin-boosting fruit and vegetables, have regular meals and a wide variety of nutrients. Avoid caffeine, smoking and even though research says one glass may not harm you, its best to cut out alcohol. Take 400mcg of folic acid daily up to week 16 to help prevent neural deficiencies. Listen to your body – if its crying out for something (apart from cigarettes, coffee and alcohol), the feel-good endorphins might be worth it. Just be sensible – don't go overboard.

Doing some gentle regular exercise is good for combating tiredness as it boosts energy levels and improves circulation in your body. (It is always a good idea to check with your GP before beginning any sort of exercise program while pregnant.)

- Yoga can be great, it improves posture, which helps to alleviate back pain or discomfort in the joints, and it increases oxygen intake and toxin expulsion, which improves general health and vitality. It is also great for relaxation and to give you time to focus on yourself and the baby. Special pregnancy yoga is also designed to strengthen and tone the pelvic floor muscles to provide good support for the increased weight of the abdomen during pregnancy. Consult a qualified yoga instructor before you start.
- Pilates is very good during pregnancy, as it helps you not only to keep your pelvic floor supple but also to regain your shape once you have given birth. Consult a qualified pilates teacher before you start.
- Avoid anything high impact (running, aerobics). Instead try walking or swimming. Swimming is one of the most relaxing and comfortable forms of exercise during pregnancy.

- Massage can have many benefits, from relieving morning sickness to easing heartburn, swollen legs and back pain. It can also help to ease anxiety over the birth and sleepless nights. It is also good for heavy legs and puffy feet and ankles. Make sure that your massage therapist is pregnancy qualified though.

Don't feel like you have to put a brave face on all the time. Let partners, friends and family give you a hand. You need to focus your energy on your growing baby and rest is the best way to rejuvenate mind, body and soul. Make time for yourself, be it a warm bath (not hot) or simply a relaxation tape, or take time to do some meditation. Pampering – time that is just for you – works wonders for morale and for well-being.

Avoid using the sauna or steam room as it can raise your body temperature too high – again, check with your GP if you are unsure.

Top Tip: Ginger settles the stomach and is great for any kind of nausea, especially morning sickness – ginger beer, ginger tea, ginger biscuits or candied ginger can all be helpful.

Stretch marks

You can do everything possible – eating right, being careful not to gain too much weight, rubbing in creams – but you might end up with stretch marks anyway. They are most likely to appear on the tummy, but are also possible on the breasts, upper arms, hips, thighs and even buttocks. The abdomen area is the most likely as it is under a lot of pressure, but all skin is at risk as a result of weight gain. Only genetics have the answer to why some women don't suffer as much as others. Having said that, there are definitely things that you can do to minimize the amount of havoc that stretch marks wreak on your body.

- Watch your weight and try to keep extra pounds under control. Stretch marks are more likely to develop when the skin is forced to stretch too rapidly. You must gain a healthy amount of weight during your pregnancy, but a slow and gradual gain is best, not only for your baby, but for your body.

- Stay well hydrated from the inside and outside, especially if you are gaining weight quickly. You are less likely to experience stretch marks if the skin is hydrated and moisturized, because skin that is supple and soft has more elastic qualities. Try to drink at least two litres of water a day and eat plenty of high water content fruit and vegetables like melon, grapefruit, strawberries, broccoli, cabbage, cauliflower, celery, aubergine, lettuce, bell peppers, radish, spinach, courgettes and tomatoes.

- Creams containing shea butter, cocoa butter, papaya extract or vitamin E can all help to reduce the appearance of stretch marks, especially if used in the early stages and all the way through the pregnancy. Avoid anything with too many chemicals or preservatives in and check with your GP if you are at all unsure whether something is safe to use

If you already have stretch marks – it's not too late to lubricate. Stretched skin that is kept supple and soft is far more likely to return to normal once your pregnancy weight is lost.

Top Tip: Two tablespoons of honey in a warm bath can help your skin to retain moisture. In the shower, wet your tummy and rub a little honey directly on to the belly. Let it remain while you shower and rinse off last of all.

Make-up

When your hormones are raging, when your body is doing all kinds of crazy things and you feel like a lump, make-up can be a fantastic pick-me-up. It can not only help you to see yourself as pretty again, but it can also give you back an element of control in your life.

Try the 'basic face' in the step-by-step make-up looks (page 173) using products that suit however your skin is behaving, as explained in the section on skin care (page 55).

Top Tip: For a quick and easy lift, just put on some blusher, the brighter the better. It's the best way to give yourself an instant boost.

Beauty and long-term illness

Dealing with any kind of long-term illness can be hard enough as it is without having to worry about what you look like as well. My approach to beauty and long-term illness is mostly an extension of my approach to beauty in general. Because my beauty 'cake recipe' theory is based on the fact that everything works as a team, it follows that concentrating on keeping the mind and body as healthy as possible – the bulk of the ingredients in the beauty 'cake' – are still the fundamental priorities. Having said that, however, as mentioned at the beginning of the section on make-up, our skin and our appearance can have quite a massive effect on our levels of self-esteem and the way that we interact with others. So a two-pronged approach is the most beneficial way to approach beauty and long-term illness.

Mind and body

When you are coping with the effects of long-term illness, stress management techniques can really help to relieve some of your symptoms. You will be physically stressed as your body fights to cope with the illness, you will also be emotionally stressed, dealing with feelings of anger, frustration, fear and possibly embarrassment.

When the body is balanced, it will try to heal itself. When the body is out of balance, it will first try to find balance. Stressful situations put the body out of balance, therefore anything that can reduce stress encourages the body to rebalance, which will give it more time and energy to invest in its own healing processes. Trying to keep the mind and body calm will not only help you to fight your illness, but it will also help you to feel and look better.

Nutrition

Eating a balanced and nutritious diet, as explained in the section on nutrition (page 24), can have an enormous effect on our general health, even more so when our body is battling to heal itself and it needs all the help that it can get. Staying away from chemicals and additives and stocking up on fresh, organic wholefoods will help a lot, as will avoiding things that agitate the body like caffeine, alcohol, sugar, salt, spices, yeast, fatty foods and cigarettes.

> Top Tip: If you are going through chemotherapy, give your digestive system a helping hand by eating soft foods that don't require it to have to work too hard to extract the nutrients. Things like fresh juices, soup, mashed potatoes, pureed vegetables, porridge, lentils, eggs, grilled or poached fish and minced chicken. Fresh fruits are also good, but citrus ones may be too acidic.

Dealing with stress

In the section on stress (page 41), there are many suggestions of techniques that can be used to help alleviate stress, including massage, reflexology, aromatherapy, yoga and exercise. These things can all really help, but should only be done with permission from your GP. Things for which you don't need permission from your doctor include:

- *Having positive experiences* Doing things that you enjoy doing can really reduce stress levels. Positive experiences give the body positive energy to counteract all the negative energy from the illness. Endorphins are released in the brain that balance out the stress response in the body and enjoying yourself can help to ease the general frustration that goes along with being ill.

- *Relaxation* Learning to relax is one of the best ways to reduce stress in our lives. Dancing, painting, reading, playing music, seeing friends or even just taking time out and having a nice bath are all things that we can do to relax. But there are also things that we can do that take the body into a deeper state of restorative relaxation, using breathing techniques to increase the amount of 'life-giving' oxygen flowing round the body. The *yoga nidra* (relaxation) section (page 216), decribes a few simple relaxation exercises that can be used to calm the body and mind in times of stress. The 'relaxation response' is another:

  - First, you need to be in a quiet place where you won't be disturbed. Assume one of the positions suitable for breathing exercises (Figure 3.17) and close your eyes, relax your body and become aware of your breathing. Breathe in through your nose and out through your mouth.

  - Then, you need to have an object or mental device to focus on. This could mean that you repeat a word or sound that will help you to feel relaxed and focused. It could mean that you look at an object that pleases you, or maybe you just concentrate on a feeling such as peace or love.

- The most important part of this exercise is that you need to learn to adopt what is called 'a passive attitude'. This involves trying to maintain focus on your object or mental device, but not allowing yourself to worry about being distracted. You accept that it is part of the process and gently guide yourself back to your point of focus. This non-judgemental response to distractions is the heart of the relaxation response exercise.
- Continue like this for ten to twenty minutes and at a certain point you should become aware that you are in a pleasant state, like the feeling you might have if you were lying on a beach on a warm summer's day. This is the relaxation response.

Skin, hair care and make-up

As mentioned above, when you are suffering from any kind of long-term illness, your self-image can take a bit of a beating. Not only are you fighting for your life, but you hardly recognize the person that you see when you look in the mirror. Your skin might have changed, your nails might feel weak and you may even be losing your hair. Even though it might be the last thing you feel like doing, try investing a little time into revamping your beauty routine, and in the process, yourself. It might just be the boost that you need to help you to feel more confident not only about yourself, but about your recovery.

Skin care

Long-term illness often takes its toll on the skin by dehydrating it and sensitizing it. So, unless you had dry and sensitive skin before you became ill, you will most likely need to take a new approach to skin care.

- First, start to combat any dehydration from the inside, by drinking at least two litres of water a day and eating lots of fluid-rich fruit and vegetables like melon, grapefruit, strawberries, broccoli, cabbage, cauliflower, celery, aubergine, lettuce, bell peppers, radish, spinach, courgettes and tomatoes.
- Secondly, adopt a new skin-care routine:
  - *Cleanse* using a mild, unfragranced creamy, water-soluble cleanser and apply it using the facial massage routine described in the section on skin care (pages 98–105). This will help to exfoliate the skin, increase the circulation and improve its texture and appearance.

- *Tone* either by splashing with cool water or with a soothing mist of rosewater. Avoid anything with alcohol as it can irritate the skin.
- *Moisturize* with something comforting and nourishing – look for ingredients like camomile, aloe vera and vitamin E. Always wear sun protection when you are outdoors.

Hair care

Like skin, the strength of your hair can can be drastically affected by long-term illness, especially if you are undergoing any kind of chemotherapy treatment. Here are some pointers for dealing with dry and weak hair.

- Use only gentle hair products, and help to prevent the scalp from becoming dry and flaky by applying a gentle unperfumed moisturizer or natural oils such as almond or olive oil. If you gently massage the scalp at the same time, you may improve the blood supply to the hair follicles, promoting healthier hair.
- Avoid using hairdryers or heated rollers, as the heat can be too drying and damage your hair, as can over-vigorous brushing. Be gentle with your hair, maybe switch to a softer baby brush, or a wide-toothed comb.
- Stick with tints or hair dyes that are made of natural colourants and avoid chemical perms as these can make your hair even more dry and brittle.
- Pony tails, plaits and tight 'up-dos' can put extra pressure on the scalp and cause irritation, as can sleeping on a nylon pillowcase. Treat yourself to a lovely soft cotton one.

Dealing with losing your hair

On top of everything else that you are having to deal with, if you end up losing you hair as well, you might feel totally lost and overwhelmed. Our hair can represent so many things and it can be a real shock to the system to have to deal with suddenly feeling so vulnerable and exposed.

It might help to talk to other people who have gone through similar experinces, and there are many support groups that can offer help and advice. I have listed some helpful contact numbers in the 'Taking it further' section at the back of the book (page 275). There are various practical things that you can do to help though:

- *Dealing with a dry scalp* This is a very common problem as a result of hair loss due to chemotherapy. Boost your internal hydration (as mentioned above) to start with, and then treat your scalp as if it were eczema condition skin. While the hair is still very short, wash your hair and scalp using an emollient or aqueous cream instead of shampoo, as any kind of shampoo can irritate the scalp at this stage. Once your hair starts to grow back, you can switch to a very mild shampoo designed for frequent use, which shouldn't dry the scalp out too much.

- *Wigs* Like make-up, wigs can give you a little bit of confidence back. They are not for everyone, but for some they can be a really great way to deal with their hair loss. They can even be an excuse to experiment with a whole new look! Take a friend with you when you go to look at wigs, someone whose opinion you really trust. And even if you are going to be bold and try something different, try to make sure that it still looks natural.

- *Diversions* There are many accessories you can wear and fashion statements that you can make that can be used to draw attention away from your hair by highlighting other things. Hats and scarves can be changed with your mood, as can jewellery and brightly coloured clothes, and they all serve to divert the eye, even if only temporarily. If they make you feel a little better about yourself, then that's the main thing.

One of the best things that you can do, however, is to go out and continue with your social life. It might be really difficult at first, and you may feel really reluctant, but as you spend more time with other people your confidence should grow and that will help you to be able to cope better.

Make-up

The great thing about make-up is that it can give you the tools to look and feel good, even when you don't. The way your face looks is one area of your life that you still have control over, and using make-up to lift your spirits can literally help you to put on a brave face.

These tips can be used as extra information to accompany the guide for the 'basic face' in the step-by-step make-up looks (page 173).

figure 4.1 eyebrow stencil

- *Base* Go for something sheer, lightweight and moisturizing – a tinted moisturizer is perfect. It has just enough tint to even out skin tone and feels light on the skin.
- *Concealer* Apply where necessary, following the guide in the clever concealing section (page 124). Be careful that the shade is not too light.
- *Powder* Just a gentle dusting of face powder will set the base in place.
- *Eyebrows* If your brows are thinner than they used to be, follow the guide in the easy eyebrows section (page 132) to fill them either with an eyebrow pencil, or eyebrow powder. If you lose your eyebrows completely and need a bit of help with the shape, you can use an eyebrow template (see Figure 4.1) as a guide. These are widely available over the internet in various shapes and sizes.

- *Highlight* Highlighter is a great way to add a bit of life and radiance back into otherwise dull and lacklustre skin. As detailed in 'how to highlight' (page 139) apply and blend to the C shape around the eyes.
- *Bronze/blush* Bronzer under the cheekbones and at the temples can help to slim down a puffy face, while a swirl of a rosy blush over the apples of the cheek blended out towards the ears gives a vibrant healthy glow.
- *Eyes* A colour wash with a pale shimmer shadow is a great way to liven-up tired eyes. Alternatively, for more definition, try some of the basic definition tips in the 'shadow secrets' section (page 152).

- *Lashes* If your lashes are thinning, use a mascara primer followed by a coat of mascara to give them a boost. This is explained more in the 'eyelash enhancing' section (page 160). Alternatively, a sweep of eyeliner can give the illusion of fuller lashes and is explained in detail in the 'movie star' section of the step-by-step make-up looks (page 177). Failing that, false eyelashes can also be used to give either a glamorous or a natural appearance. They are great for special occasions, but may be a bit fiddly for every day. Details on how best to apply them can be found on page 165.

- *Lips* Colour on the lips can help to balance the face. Go for something creamy and moisturizing and not too pale, and either dab it on with fingers for a soft, natural look, or follow the tips in the 'luscious lips' section (page 166) for a more polished pout.

05

the secret ingredients: the real source of beauty

In this chapter you will learn:
- how to explore your vision of your own beauty
- how to make simple changes to bring more happiness into your life

Self-esteem *(learn to like yourself and discover your own beauty)*

Having the tools of make-up to help you to look your best can be a great confidence booster, especially on days when we feel down and unattractive, and hopefully this book will provide you with those tools. If we are really going to reach our maximum beauty potential, however, we want to unlock that confident, killer beauty that doesn't get painted on, but radiates from within.

It is inside all of us, but most of us are just so preoccupied trying to be someone else that we don't even acknowledge it. We get stuck in a world full of glossy magazines and celebrity gossip and it is very easy for us to forget that it's not real. We are endlessly comparing ourselves and judging ourselves, and this endless cycle stops us from accepting who we really are and therefore actually fulfilling our own beauty potential.

Not accepting yourself for who you are means that you will always feel incomplete; you will always be looking for ways to fill the void. You might try to cover it up with a mask of make-up, or fantastic hair, you may even have botox or plastic surgery in an attempt to project to the world that you are something or someone other than yourself.

In doing this, even though you might be doing it to 'look good', you are actually sending a message to the world that you don't find yourself beautiful – so how is the world suppose to find you beautiful? They may think that your make-up looks great, but is this a hamster wheel that you want to ride for the rest of your life?

If someone comes up to you and says 'You look great tonight', you think it's going to give your confidence a boost, and on the surface, it probably does, but underneath your subconscious is thinking, 'I did a good job of my make-up today' – it's not actually thinking that you look great! You can get caught in a cycle of then only feeling confident behind the mask and living in fear of anyone seeing you without it, and any confidence that you may have had without it before, will be overridden by this fear and the need for the mask will increase until your self-esteem just gets weaker and weaker.

It takes much more energy to be what you are not, and living in denial of yourself is a constant mental and emotional stress, the effects of which are completely detrimental to both your health and your beauty. The section on stress (page 41) explains these effects in more detail.

Accepting who you are and being honest with yourself will stop you from filling your life with negative energy and a negative self-image. It will boost your self-esteem from the inside rather than the outside, which in itself will project a more beautiful 'you'. You will be able to realize your own true beauty potential as opposed to a projected or expected beauty standard. Then, instead of being a mask to hide behind, your make-up truly will be the icing on the cake.

How to accept yourself and discover your own beauty

- Get to know yourself. Ask yourself these questions:
  - Who am I?
  - When am I most happy?
  - When am I most confident?
  - When am I least stressed?
- Use your answers as stepping stones on the pathway to becoming more self-aware.
- Remember beauty is created from the inside out, and you need to get to know who you really are, as opposed to the 'you' that you think others want you to be.
- Stop giving yourself marks out of ten or comparing yourself to others – it drains self-esteem and confidence.
- Find out what you like about yourself. The key to thinking yourself beautiful is to focus on the things about yourself that you like and learn how to love yourself.
- Remember that individuality is one of the keys to real beauty and the goal of building self-esteem is to not see yourself or anyone else as either inferior or superior, and to have no fear of approval or disapproval.
- Finally, look in the mirror, and ask yourself: 'What is beautiful about me?' Find one attractive thing about yourself – eyelashes, nails, ears or knees – whatever. Do the same thing for a week looking for a different thing each day.
- You can then use make-up to enhance those features. Advice and tips about make-up and how to apply it, are contained in the section on make-up (page 112).

- We often judge ourselves very harshly. Learn to be your own best friend: look at yourself with a warm heart.
- Remember that self-discovery won't come overnight, but once you start the journey you are on the path towards to a happier life and towards your own beauty.

Happiness *(think happy, be happy)*

Having a healthy and positive attitude towards life is just as important in the beauty recipe as all the other ingredients. We already know that everything is interlinked, and that the mind affects the body, which affects skin and so on.

Having a positive attitude towards life can have such a massive effect on the way that we feel about ourselves and this inevitably also has a direct effect on how we look. Happy people are perceived as more attractive and more popular than people who are not happy. A happy face is usually a glowing and beautiful one. A happy face needs very little make-up to enhance it because it is already radiating the kind of sparkle that I'm usually trying to create when I do someone's make-up. A positive attitude puts a smile on your lips, a light in your eyes and a spring in your step that that can't be bought or painted on, because it comes from the inside. All we have to remember is that happiness is inside all of us; we just have to choose it.

Ten ways to have a happy day

1 Get up – even if you would rather stay in bed.
2 Decide that you are going to have a good day.
3 Stretch and breathe in slowly and deeply – imagine breathing out any negative feelings as you exhale. There are more exercises in the breathing section on yoga.
4 Eat breakfast and drink some water and fresh juice if possible.
5 Think of someone you love and who loves you. Feel that warmth and keep it with you all day.
6 Prioritize and only do what is necessary – don't try to do too much.
7 Wear something bright – I have a bright green and purple skirt that one of my best friends brought me back from India and every time I wear it people come up to me and say, 'I love your skirt, it's really brightened my day!' They smile at me and that makes me feel happy!

8 Be good to yourself: have a massage or a long bath.

> Top Tip: A way to be good to yourself *and* be more beautiful is to take ten minutes to lie down and relax with either cucumber slices or cotton wool pads soaked in rosewater placed over your eyes. This is an instant stress reliever and beautifier in one!

9 Make an effort with your appearance: do your hair, put on some make-up, wear a nice outfit – it always gets a positive response from people. For make-up advice and tips on how to apply, please see the section on make-up (page 112).

10 Smile. Smiling not only releases happy chemicals in our own brains, it will often start a chain reaction of cheering up the people around us, which then comes back to us again. So it works like a double dose!

Ten ways to cheer yourself up if you are down in the dumps

1 List your ten favourite things to do and make plans to do at least one this week.

2 Achieve something, even if it's just the washing-up. Achievement gives you a sense of control.

3 Play some music that you like – it is both relaxing and mentally stimulating

4 Dance. Dancing not only gets the circulation going, but it is also expressive and is a great way to release tension. Just like when we exercise, endorphins, the brain's happy hormones, are released in the brain.

5 Spend a day doing what you want to do rather than what you feel you ought to do.

6 Make a 'Happy box': a collection of letters and pictures, etc. to look through when you are down in the dumps.

7 Find something to laugh about – phone a funny friend or rent a funny movie. Laughter makes the brain release chemicals that relax the blood vessels, it reduces levels of the stress hormones adrenaline and cortisol in the blood, and it increases circulation (boosting oxygen and nutrient intake).

8 Phone a long-lost friend for a chat (not a moan). Talking with friends releases oxytocin in the brain (another of the brain's happy chemicals).

9 Expand your senses: lie in a field or park – smell the flowers, listen to the birds, feel the breeze, see the blue of the sky.

10 Paint a picture. Even if you don't think of yourself as creative. The process forces you to focus and concentrate. It relaxes the mind and body and you come away with a sense of achievement.

Ten ways to make your life happier

1 Live in the present: let go of the past. Live in the moment. Forget about the past or the future; try not to dwell on hurts or worries that might never happen or have already taken place. Learn to appreciate the here and now, and simple pleasures.

2 Think happy: your thoughts, not your circumstances, dictate how you feel. A happy outlook encourages the production of endorphins, which create a feeling of well-being. They are also thought to stimulate the body's defences and repair mechanisms which will have a positive effect on the way you look and feel. Fresh ideas come from a fresh mind – clear your head – maybe go for a walk or just get some fresh air.

3 Remember that you are not alone. Almost everyone you know has days when they feel down and overwhelmed by life. Knowing that you are not the only one feeling like this can sometimes make it a bit easier to deal with.

4 Understand your moods – try to be aware of yourself and try to avoid reacting or making decisions when you are in a low mood. Also, accept that everyone has mood swings. This doesn't mean that we have to accept abuse, but rather than getting upset, we can make allowances in our minds and hearts for not only our own, but other people's moods.

5 Understand that we can't change others, what we can change is our own perception of others. Accepting that everyone is an individual can mean that life becomes more peaceful.

6 Try to enjoy your job as much as possible. A fulfilling career does wonders for general well-being. If work is not quite as fulfilling as you would like it to be, try to have at least one hobby, preferably an active one.

7 Try not to be negative – try to turn negatives into positives and life will be much more positive. Take time out to isolate your thoughts and ask yourself, 'Does this have to be negative or can I make this into something positive?'

8 If you need to be right more than you need to be happy, it might be time to relax some of your opinions.

9 Stop giving yourself marks out of ten or comparing yourself to others – it drains self-esteem and confidence. Try to be your own best friend.

10 Life is what happens to you while you are busy making other plans. If you find yourself thinking 'I'll be happy when...' you are missing out. You can be happy right now – just choose it.

06

keeping the cake fresh: wisdom to pass on...

In this chapter you will learn:
- words of wisdom from celebrity and non-celebrity clients
- details and addresses of various organizations and specialists
- extra information about nutrients in food

Words of wisdom

To get this chapter going, I asked my husband, actor, James Redmond to give me the male take on female beauty. 'Ah, women and beauty. Mmmmmm...' he said.

'Most of my male friends prefer a lady who looks "natural", healthy and above all confident. It doesn't matter if she's curvy or slim, it's the confidence that counts; it's the confidence that's attractive. A healthy lifestyle breeds confidence. If you watch your diet and get some exercise, your skin, hair and figure should improve and you won't need to wear much make-up, or even have plastic surgery. You can also wear sexier clothes. Please. You'll look and feel great and you'll know it. Nice one.'

I also asked if he had any comment on the subject of male grooming:

'As for us blokes, we're trying our best. After all, we've got to appear not to care and that's not easy. The phrase "male grooming" is heard a lot more these days and no longer has the connotations of our fathers' day. So, David Bowie, we thank you (not sure about the lip gloss though!). I've been playing football all my life and when I started "cleansing, toning and moisturizing" at my model agent's request back in 1994, I had to watch my back in the changing room, so to speak. However, these days even the midfield hard men are doing it.

I've continued my routine into my acting career and I'm proud to say that, unlike most of my male colleagues, I don't need to visit the make-up chair before filming. I do however have a small problem with eczema, aggravated by eating too many dairy products and playing football in nylon socks. Obviously I'm lucky to have Yvette to cook me delicious, healthy meals and encourage me to drink more water, but it's my dedication to football and hygiene that really helps. I may not actually get the ball much, but I did a Cruyff turn last week and I never forget my wash bag.'

I had the pleasure of working with Tamzin Outhwaite on a shoot for the *Radio Times* when Hotel Babylon first came onto our screens. She told me that her favourite trick to looking good is when she is applying a 'full' make-up: 'to keep my skin really dewy by moisturizing heavily and not powdering the face too much, or even at all. This makes the skin look younger! Hooray!'

The last time that I worked on a beauty shoot for *Good Housekeeping*, I cornered Tamara Corin, Deputy Beauty Editor, and got her to tell me a couple of her favourite tips. The first was to 'buy a small plastic pump spray and fill it with water and add a couple of drops of peppermint oil. Pop this into your handbag for an instant all-over refresher. Great in the sticky summer months!' The second was a great way to fake a perfect manicure: 'Soak your nails in lemon juice to remove any stains, then use a nail buffer to make tips shiny. No polish required!'

I first worked with Bill Nighy when he was doing press and promotion for the film *Love Actually*. His skin was in great condition and he was very easy to groom. When I asked him if he had any words of wisdom on the subject of male grooming, he told me: 'I think it's safe to say that real men moisturize these days and that not smoking remains a boy's best friend.'

When *Cutting It* star, Christine Stephen-Daly used to work on *Casualty*, I did her make-up for a very glamorous Christmas Special shoot for *OK* magazine, and she told me that when it comes to skin care, there are two products that she can't live without: 'Alcohol-free facial cleansing wipes and a good moisturizer.' She told me that she uses the wipes 'for taking off make-up, before cleansing, as they are brilliant for removing every last scrap of make-up – including water-proof mascara'. She also said that 'moisturizer is a very personal thing, but it's the only product, in my opinion, where it's necessary to spend a little more. I don't mean that you have to buy the most expensive brands, though, as there are plenty of great mid-price range moisturizers'.

Hair expert Charlotte Murray from Murray and Mace (bespoke hair and make-up) told me that 'communication is the key' to getting the best haircut. 'Take pictures of hair textures, colours, lengths and attitude from magazines to your hairdresser and talk about them with your stylist. Using them as a guide, they will be able to create something that is tailor-made for you.' When it comes to choosing a stylist for your wedding day: 'Always have a trial and give the stylist as much information as you can about the look that you want to create.'

When I asked my yoga teacher, Lara Baumann, founder of the Quantum method of yoga, if she had anything to say on the subject of beauty, she told me that it's really all about accepting who we really are and that 'beauty is the true self that shines forth when the misidentification with that which is not real has been overcome and the individual realizes the state of union or yoga'.

I asked Daniel Sandler, co-founder of Daniel Sandler cosmetics, and make-up artist to the stars, if he would divulge a couple of his trade secrets and he gave me these great tips: 'Double up your blusher by rubbing a little on your lips, then layering lip balm on top. Your lip colour will perfectly match your cheeks, and it's one less product to carry! Also, if you have blonde hair and dark eyebrows, try applying a gold eye shadow onto your brows to tone in with your golden locks.'

Penny Jones is an artist who looks 20 years younger than she actually is and says that her secret is 'water, water water!' and that it is important 'to drink plenty throughout the day'.

Fashion model Suzannah Agrippa knows what it's like to have to get ready in a rush, and she told me:

'My long-term beauty plan is to moisturize, hydrate and condition, however, in this busy world sometimes we all need a "quick fix". Just before running out to a casting, I whip out my magic make-up: an all-in-one lip, cheek and eyelid tint with just a hint of colour to give you an instant rosy warmth and add freshness to your skin. You don't need to be a Da Vinci to apply it either!'

I couldn't even contemplate writing about how to shape your eyebrows without consulting with Shavata, eyebrow expert and founder of the Brow Studio at the Urban Retreat, Harrods. She told me that 'shaping your brows can instantly "lift" your features and take years off you'. She agrees that 'if you're not really sure where to start, visit a professional who will give you a good starting shape which you can then pluck, ideally on a daily basis, to keep it'. Also, a great idea is to 'take a picture of a celebrity with you when you visit your therapist to give her an idea of the look you would like. Your therapist will be able to advise you on how to re-create a celebrity's eyebrow shape whilst ensuring that it will suit the shape of your face.'

When I made-up Georgina Bouzova for a fashion shoot for *Now* magazine, her character on *Casualty* was married to my husband's character which was a bit of a weird one! Luckily we got along really well and she gave me some great beauty advice. She told me that recently she had 'really cut back on caffeine and alcohol' and every morning she drinks 'a glass of hot water with lemon squeezed into it'. She told me that 'since I started doing this, my skin has looked a lot better' and 'a lot of my friends have even commented on this'. I also asked if she had any top tips for dealing with stress and she told me that regular reflexology has really helped her to get through 'filming a very emotional storyline', adding that 'it seems to balance me emotionally and help keep me on an even keel after such roller coaster of feelings'.

I asked Sally Penford, the Education Manager at the International Dermal Institute for her tips about choosing sun protection cream. She advises to 'look for products which are oil-free to avoid congesting the skin'. She also says that creams 'which contain anti-oxidants such as grape-seed, vitamins A, C and E and super-oxide dismutase will protect the skin against free-radical damage, therefore delaying the signs of ageing'.

One of my beautiful brides, Anna Byas, gave me this great tip for making a fantastic de-stress lavender bath:

'Put some freshly picked lavender into a microwave-proof container and cover it with water. Zap it on high in the microwave for one minute, give it a stir and then zap it again for another minute. Let the mixture sit for a few minutes before draining the liquid off and pouring it into your bath. It makes the water a lovely colour and smells divine.'

A great way to use up the leftover lavender is to put it 'into a thin flannel (or you could use a piece of muslin), tie it up and use it to exfoliate the skin'.

Marc Ramos at Brooks and Brooks Hairdressers is my brilliant hair colourist and his advice for colour-treated hair is this:

'To help stop colour from fading use protein-based treatments as these help to strengthen the hair and lock in colour. To create natural shine on your colour, camomile-based shampoos are best. To refresh colour, especially if you are going to a party, try using colour-treated shampoos and conditioners. Don't use them too often though, as the colour pigments can build up and make the hair dull. Maintain your colour: every six weeks for block colours and every eight weeks for highlights. This will ensure you will always have beautiful and glamorous hair.'

I thought that I knew every trick in the book until my favourite beauty therapist Rebecca Cawse, told me this brilliant way to stop you from getting lipstick on your teeth: 'finish applying your lipstick and then suck your finger like a lollypop'. As you pull your finger out of your mouth, it 'will remove all traces of colour from inside your lips'.

While she was pregnant with her baby Jessica, Alison Potter, my best friend from university, told me, 'Most women glow at some point in their pregnancy. My hair got thicker and glossier, my eyes brighter and my skin clearer – if only someone could bottle it then I'd order a lifetime's supply.'

Lainey Sheridan-Young owns her own fashion sales and PR company, and I have done her make-up on several occasions for various magazines, including *Vogue*, *Tatler* and *YOU* magazine. Her beauty secret is to 'focus on the things that you love' about yourself, and also to 'learn to love the things that you hate'. She says that 'you get much more confidence from looking in the mirror and focusing on things that you like about yourself, rather than obsessing about the things that you want to change', but she also says, that 'a big nose, gappy teeth or scars are what make a person unique and special, and therefore beautiful. Once you can learn to love the bits you hate, your confidence will grow enormously'. She told me:

> 'I learned this ten years ago after a motorbike accident left me with 32 stitches in my face and black eyes – I had plasters all over my face except on my nose and rather than hating the damaged bits, I suddenly appreciated and loved my nose (something I had never done before!) The remaining scars make me unique!'

When I wanted to find someone to give me some advice about hair, there was only one person that I could ask: Paul Merritt, Co-Director of Bloww with whom I worked on Channel 4's *The Salon*. His advice for keeping your hair in tip-top condition is:

> 'Once a week, give your hair a day off from styling products and heat; try using a deep conditioning mask and then leaving your hair to dry naturally – it will mean that your hair is able to maintain its natural strength and shine and ultimately keep looking its best.'

He also gave me this great tip:

> 'If you're thinking about changing hairdressers but aren't confident in what you're looking for, visit a few different ones for blow dries so as to gain a little understanding of their capabilities and see how you get on with them as a person. This will probably help you to make up your mind!'

Journalist Sarah Feeley told me that her life has changed since I introduced her to foundation primer. She said:

'However carefully I used to apply my make-up, it would never last. It would always slide down my face, or even disappear completely, leaving me bare-faced and feeling exposed. Now my make-up stays put, but the primer is so light that my skin can still breathe and my make-up looks natural. Most importantly, I don't worry about it anymore. It's confidence in a bottle.'

She even gave me this great bit of advice from her mum, Sue Feeley, who says, 'I find foundation too heavy, especially in the summer, so I mix a little bit of foundation with my moisturizer, which I find gives a much more even coverage and doesn't feel cakey.'

I met Alison Frecknall on a shoot for *Prima* magazine and she told me that:

'Coping with breast (or any other) cancer is hard enough, so the side-effects of the treatment can often feel like Mother Nature's final slap in the face! Added to the impact that the surgery has on your body image, there is the hair loss from chemo, the bloating from steroids and, with some forms of long-term drug therapy, unavoidable weight gain. And whether you are 25 or 45, chemotherapy can throw you into the menopause. It's easy for your self-image as a woman to sink like a stone, but I was lucky; a makeover from Yvette for a magazine photo shoot, followed by a beauty session through the marvellous "Look Good Feel Better" scheme run by Maggie's cancer charity made me realize the psychological benefits that a beauty regime can bring. Top tips? Always remember that self-image rests in the spiritual, not the physical, and ... get an eyebrow sculpting kit; magic even when your own eyebrows have bailed out on you!'

The final words in this chapter have to go to my own mother, Yvonne Iles. I have been cleansing, toning and moisturizing religiously ever since my thirteenth birthday when she gave me a posh set of skin-care products and I shall be eternally grateful for those good foundations! I asked her if she had any trade secrets from her days as a dancer and a model and she told me:

'Really good false eyelashes and very little make-up used to look really good on television, but even though the lighting has changed so much and the products are so fine now, blending your foundation with a dry brush or your fingers still works the best.'

And any general tips? 'I have washed my body with a scratchy exfoliating mitt since I was 18 and I think that it really makes a difference to your circulation and it definitely helps with cellulite.' Oh yes, and, 'Drink water, don't smoke and don't go to bed with your make-up on. Did I ever tell you?' Yes mum, you did – sound familiar?

Appendix

Nutrients

Allicin This is a powerful anti-bacterial and anti-viral agent, which helps to combat infection and boosts the immune system. It also helps to prevent blood clots and it can lower blood pressure and blood cholesterol. It can also lift the mood and has a mild calming effect.

Beta-glucan This is a soluble fibre, which enhances the immune system and lowers blood cholesterol.

Bromelain This aids digestion, helps dissolve blood clots and is good for preventing osteoporosis and bone fractures because of its very high manganese content. It is also antibacterial, anti-inflammatory and anti-viral.

Calcium Calcium works alongside vitamin C to make collagen and other nutrients to keep the skin healthy. It keeps bones and teeth strong, ensures proper functioning of muscles and nerves and it even helps your blood clot.

Capsicum Capsicum increases circulation and helps all the nutrients to be taken into the bloodstream quicker.

Carotenoids Carotenoids are highly-coloured plant pigments that have high antioxidant effects. They collect in the skin and provide what dermatologists call a 'parasol' effect, deflecting some of the harmful UV rays from the sun. Beta-carotene (which the body converts into vitamin A) is found in orange foods, lutein in yellow (and some green) foods, and lycopene in red foods.

Coenzyme Q-10 This is a natural vitamin-like substance that acts as an antioxidant. It stimulates the circulation, boosts the immune system and has powerful anti-ageing capabilities.

Copper Copper is an essential trace mineral and antioxidant enzyme that protects cells against the effects of free radicals. It works in partnership to strengthen the power of antioxidant vitamins, helps the body to utilize iron, maintains the health of your bones and connective tissues, helps the body produce the pigment melanin and keeps the thyroid gland functioning normally. For more information on melanin, please refer to the section on the sun (page 13).

Fatty acids　　Omega 3 and 6 help to keep the skin soft and stop it from dehydrating. They absorb fat-soluble vitamins, maintain moisture and repair tissue. This helps to plump-up the skin and reduce fine lines. They are also known to be anti-inflammatory, anti-coagulant and exhibit anti-cancer activity.

Ferulic acid　　This is an antioxidant made by plants to protect themselves from UV rays – it has the same effect on skin.

Flavinoids　　Flavinoids have potent antioxidant properties, which may help to lower cholesterol levels in the blood. Also, some evidence suggests that flavinoids have some effect on blood platelets making them less sticky, so possibly reducing the risk of a blood clot.

Glutathione　　This is a powerful antioxidant that is also important for detoxification because it binds to toxins, such as heavy metals, solvents and pesticides, and transforms them so that the body is able to dispose of them.

Iron　　Iron transports oxygen in the blood to the skin and other tissues in the body and is required by the liver in order for it to function properly. Note: women lose twice as much iron as men and are more likely to be deficient, particularly during childbearing years.

Isoflavones　　These mimic the action of oestrogen. They help to repair collagen and elastin in the skin, slow down the rate of thinning and produce lubricating oils. They also reduce the risk of osteoporosis.

Lecithin　　This is a crucial building block in cell walls which helps to keep the skin watertight. Good for daily repair and strengthening.

Lignan　　This is an antioxidant that mimics the action of oestrogen by helping to repair collagen and elastin in the skin, slowing down the rate of thinning and producing lubricating oils.

Manganese　　Manganese is an essential trace mineral and antioxidant enzyme that protects cells against the effects of free radicals. It works in partnership to strengthen the power of antioxidant vitamins. It helps the body synthesize fatty acids and cholesterol. It keeps the bones strong and healthy and helps to maintain normal blood sugar levels. It promotes optimal function of your thyroid gland and keeps the nerves healthy.

Magnesium   Important for cell repair and renewal. It can also help to balance the hormones and counteract the effects of stress on the body.

Oleic acid   Sometimes called omega 9, oleic acid is a fatty acid that increases the absorption of fat-soluble vitamins like vitamins A, E, D and K, which are essential to good health. It has antioxidant properties and can lower blood levels of cholesterol.

Polyphenols   These are the purple pigment that has antioxidant properties and also helps to strengthen capillaries and maintain blood flow. Resveratrol is the polyphenol that is in red wine, which means that one glass per day can be beneficial to your health (more than one and the free radical effect of the alcohol takes over).

Potassium   Potassium is needed by the body to keep normal water balance between the cells and body fluids, to transmit nerve impulses, to enable the contraction of muscles and to regulate blood pressure. Symptoms of potassium deficiency include fatigue, slow reflexes, muscle weakness and dry skin.

Protein amino acids   These help to repair and strengthen cell structure and stimulate the production of collagen and elastin, which keeps the skin supple. Eating protein at every meal is an important anti-ageing strategy.

Quercetin   This is a powerful antioxidant. It thins the blood, lowers cholesterol, wards off blood clots, fights asthma, chronic bronchitis, hay fever, diabetes, atherosclerosis and infections. It also has anti-inflammatory, antibiotic and antiviral properties. Quercetin can also have sedative properties.

Selenium   Selenium is an essential trace mineral and antioxidant enzyme that protects cells against the effects of free radicals. It works in partnership to strengthen the power of antioxidant vitamins. Selenium is also essential for normal functioning of the immune system and thyroid gland, as well as the production of the antioxidant enzyme glutathione.

Silicic acid/silica   This is needed to make the spongy cells in the skin that lie between the collagen and the elastin.

Sulphur   Sulphur contains important anti-aging enzymes and helps to rid the body of toxins.

Vitamin A (retinol and beta-carotene)   Vitamin A is needed for the formation of red blood cells, which carry oxygen around the body. It is necessary for tissue development. Note: a lack of vitamin A can result in dry, rough or thick skin.

Vitamins B6 and B12   These are needed for the formation of red blood cells, which carry oxygen around the body. They also help repair and rebuild tissue and are essential for healthy nerve function.

Vitamin C (ascorbic acid)   This is an antioxidant. It is needed for the formation of collagen (see skin), aids in the absorption of iron, helps the body to manufacture glutathione and is needed to maintain the healthy functioning of blood vessels, bones and teeth.

Vitamin D   This boosts the body's defence mechanism. Vitamin D is often at its lowest in winter as it is partly manufactured in the body with the help of sunlight.

Vitamin E (alpha tocopherol)   This protects skin cells against stress and injury, helps to slow cell deterioration and protects against ageing. It also helps the body to regenerate vitamin C, so together, vitamins C and E are a crucial anti-ageing double act. It is also thought to protect against chest pain and artery damage. Note: It doesn't stand up very well to processing – 90 per cent of the vitamin E in wheat is lost when it's refined into white flour.

Vitamin K   This thins the blood, making it flow more freely and thus improving the supply of nutrients.

Zinc   Zinc is an essential trace mineral and antioxidant enzyme that protects cells against the effects of free radicals. It works in partnership to strengthen the power of antioxidant vitamins. It is also necessary for collagen production and, therefore, for healthy skin.

Information

Cancer

Cancer BACUP Access has information on all aspects of cancer, written specifically for cancer patients, their families and carers. Plus over 1,000 cancer questions and answers available online. www.cancerbackup.org.uk

Cancer Counselling Trust offers free face-to-face and telephone counselling sessions to cancer patients, their family or friends and also offers support if a friend or relative has died of cancer. The trust is staffed by a team of experienced cancer counsellors. www.cctrust.org.uk

Look Good ... Feel Better is a free, non-medical, brand-neutral, national public service programme founded in 1989 to help women offset appearance-related changes from cancer treatment. www.lookgoodfeelbetter.org

Skin

The *British Association of Dermatologists* is the only professional organization representing skin specialists in the United Kingdom and Ireland. 19 Fitzroy Square, London W1P 5HQ. 0207 383 0266 www.bad.org.uk

Talk Eczema is a free information and support site for eczema sufferers and their families. www.talkeczema.com

Information and support on acne, including top ten tips, beauty tips and problems. www.stopspots.org

Make-up and skin care

Avene
For stockists: 0845 117 0116

BECCA
For stockists: 020 7556 9066
www.beccacosmetics.com

Benefit
For stockists: 0901 113 0001
www.benefitcosmetic.com

Bobbi Brown
For stockists: 0870 034 2566
www.bobbibrowncosmetics.com

Clinique
For stockists: 0870 034 2566
www.clinique.com

Couvrance
For stockists: 0845 117 0116

Crème de la Mer
For stockists: 0870 034 2566

Dermalogica
For stockists: 0800 591 818
www.dermalogica.co.uk

Daniel Sandler
For stockists: 020 7893 8333
www.danielsandler.com

E. Funkhouser
For stockists: 01908 629 466
www.efunkhouser.com

Elemis
For stockists: 01278 727 830
www.elemis.com

ESPA
For stockists: 01252 352 231
www.espaonline.com

Estée Lauder
For stockists: 0870 034 2566
www.esteelauder.com

Girogio Armani Cosmetics
Harvey Nichols: 020 7201 8687
Selfridges: 020 7318 2486

Guerlain
For stockists: 01932 233 909
www.guerlain.com

Hard Candy
For stockists: 08450 708090
www.hardcandy.com

La Prairie
For stockists: 020 8398 5300
For mail order: 020 7730 1234
www.laprairie.com

Laura Mercier
Space NK: 0208 740 2085
www.lauramercier.com

Model co.
For stockists: 020 7299 4999
www.spacenk.com

Nuxe
www.boutiqueperfumes.co.uk
www.nuxe.com

Prescriptives
For stockists: 0870 034 2566

Screen Face
020 7221 8289
www.screenface.com

Shu uemura
For stockists: 0207 235 2375
www.shuuemura.com

Stila
For stockists: 01730 232 566
www.stilacosmetics.com

Shavata, Eyebrow Expert
Urban Retreat at Harrods, London: 020 7893 8333
Urban Retreat at Harvey Nichols, Manchester: 0161 828 8856
www.shavata.co.uk

Too Faced
For stockists: 0781 220 4141
www.toofaced.com

Tweezerman
020 7410 1667
www.tweezerman.com

Urban Decay
Debenhams: 08445 61 61 61
www.urbandecay.com

Yves Saint Laurent
For stockists: 01444 255 700
www.ysl.com

Hair salons

BLOWW
4 Regent Place
London W1B 5EA
020 7292 0300

Brooks and Brooks
13–15 Sicilian Avenue
London WC1A 2QH
020 7405 8111

General

Carol Hayes Management is one of London's leading agencies representing hair stylists, make-up artists, still life, interior and fashion stylists in the industry.

5–6 Underhill Street,
London NW1 7HS
0207 482 1555
www.carolhayesmanagement.co.uk

Murray and Mace
Bespoke Hair and Make-up
0774 738 7772
www.murrayandmace.co.uk

Quantum Yoga with Lara Baumann
Om Station 3, 123 Ladbroke Grove
London W11 1PN
020 7221 5073
www.larayoga.com

Relate
Successful, healthy relationships are essential for fulfilling, stress-free lives.
0845 456 1310
www.relate.org.uk

The British Nutrition Foundation is a scientific and educational charity that promotes the well being of society through the impartial interpretation and effective dissemination of evidence-

based nutritional knowledge and advice.
020 7404 6504
www.nutrition.org.uk

Further reading

Appleton, Katy, (2005) *Yoga in Practice*, Pan
Baumann, L., (2002) *Cosmetic Dermatology*, McGraw-Hill
Baumann, L. and Will, J., (1999) *The Food Bible*, Fireside
Benson, Herbert, (2000) *The Relaxation Response*,
  Avon Books
Gross, Denis, (2006) *Your Future Face*, Plume Publishing
Guiliano, Mireille, (2006) *French Women Don't Get Fat*,
  Vintage
Hewitt, James, (1988) *The Complete Yoga Book*,
  Schocken Books
Hoggard, Liz, (2005) *How To Be Happy*, BBC Books
Holford, Patrick, (2004) *The Optimum Nutrition Bible*,
  Piatkus Books
Looker, Terry and Gregson, Olga, (2003) *Teach Yourself
  Managing Stress*, Hodder Arnold
Martin, E., (2004) *Oxford Dictionary of Nursing*, OUP
McGraw, Phil, (2004) *Self Matters*, OUP
Moriyama, Naomi, (2006) *Japanese Women Don't Get Old or
  Fat*, Vermilion
Murray, Michael and Pizzorno, Joseph, (1998) *Encyclopaedia
  of Natural Medicine*, Diane Pub Co
Robinson, Lynne, (2002) *The Official Body Control Pilates
  Manual*, Macmillan
Rosenberg, Nancy, (2003) *Outwitting Stress*,
  The Lyons Press
Ross, J. and Wilson, K. (2006) *Anatomy and Physiology*,
  Churchill Livingstone
Sullivan, Karen, (1998) *Vitamins and Minerals –
  An Illustrated Guide*, Element Books

American Academy of Dermatology:
www.aad.org/default.htm

Cancer Research UK SunSmart:
www.cancerresearchuk.org/sunsmart

The Skin Cancer Foundation:
www.skincancer.org

The Tea Council:
www.teacouncil.co.uk

index

teach yourself ®

From Advanced Sudoku to Zulu, you'll find everything you need in the **teach yourself** range, in books, on CD and on DVD.

Visit **www.teachyourself.co.uk** for more details.

Advanced Sudoku and Kakuro
Afrikaans
Alexander Technique
Algebra
Ancient Greek
Applied Psychology
Arabic
Aromatherapy
Art History
Astrology
Astronomy
AutoCAD 2004
AutoCAD 2007
Ayurveda
Baby Massage and Yoga
Baby Signing
Baby Sleep
Bach Flower Remedies
Backgammon
Ballroom Dancing
Basic Accounting
Basic Computer Skills
Basic Mathematics
Beauty
Beekeeping
Beginner's Arabic Script
Beginner's Chinese Script
Beginner's Dutch
Beginner's French

Beginner's German
Beginner's Greek
Beginner's Greek Script
Beginner's Hindi
Beginner's Italian
Beginner's Japanese
Beginner's Japanese Script
Beginner's Latin
Beginner's Mandarin Chinese
Beginner's Portuguese
Beginner's Russian
Beginner's Russian Script
Beginner's Spanish
Beginner's Turkish
Beginner's Urdu Script
Bengali
Better Bridge
Better Chess
Better Driving
Better Handwriting
Biblical Hebrew
Biology
Birdwatching
Blogging
Body Language
Book Keeping
Brazilian Portuguese
Bridge
British Empire, The

British Monarchy from Henry VIII, The
Buddhism
Bulgarian
Business Chinese
Business French
Business Japanese
Business Plans
Business Spanish
Business Studies
Buying a Home in France
Buying a Home in Italy
Buying a Home in Portugal
Buying a Home in Spain
C++
Calculus
Calligraphy
Cantonese
Car Buying and Maintenance
Card Games
Catalan
Chess
Chi Kung
Chinese Medicine
Christianity
Classical Music
Coaching
Cold War, The
Collecting
Computing for the Over 50s
Consulting
Copywriting
Correct English
Counselling
Creative Writing
Cricket
Croatian
Crystal Healing
CVs
Czech
Danish
Decluttering
Desktop Publishing
Detox
Digital Home Movie Making
Digital Photography
Dog Training
Drawing
Dream Interpretation
Dutch
Dutch Conversation
Dutch Dictionary
Dutch Grammar
Eastern Philosophy
Electronics
English as a Foreign Language
English for International Business
English Grammar
English Grammar as a Foreign Language
English Vocabulary
Entrepreneurship
Estonian
Ethics
Excel 2003
Feng Shui
Film Making
Film Studies
Finance for Non-Financial Managers
Finnish
First World War, The
Fitness
Flash 8
Flash MX
Flexible Working
Flirting
Flower Arranging
Franchising
French
French Conversation
French Dictionary
French Grammar
French Phrasebook
French Starter Kit
French Verbs
French Vocabulary
Freud
Gaelic
Gardening

Genetics
Geology
German
German Conversation
German Grammar
German Phrasebook
German Verbs
German Vocabulary
Globalization
Go
Golf
Good Study Skills
Great Sex
Greek
Greek Conversation
Greek Phrasebook
Growing Your Business
Guitar
Gulf Arabic
Hand Reflexology
Hausa
Herbal Medicine
Hieroglyphics
Hindi
Hindi Conversation
Hinduism
History of Ireland, The
Home PC Maintenance and
  Networking
How to DJ
How to Run a Marathon
How to Win at Casino Games
How to Win at Horse Racing
How to Win at Online Gambling
How to Win at Poker
How to Write a Blockbuster
Human Anatomy & Physiology
Hungarian
Icelandic
Improve Your French
Improve Your German
Improve Your Italian
Improve Your Spanish
Improving Your Employability
Indian Head Massage

Indonesian
Instant French
Instant German
Instant Greek
Instant Italian
Instant Japanese
Instant Portuguese
Instant Russian
Instant Spanish
Internet, The
Irish
Irish Conversation
Irish Grammar
Islam
Italian
Italian Conversation
Italian Grammar
Italian Phrasebook
Italian Starter Kit
Italian Verbs
Italian Vocabulary
Japanese
Japanese Conversation
Java
JavaScript
Jazz
Jewellery Making
Judaism
Jung
Kama Sutra, The
Keeping Aquarium Fish
Keeping Pigs
Keeping Poultry
Keeping a Rabbit
Knitting
Korean
Latin
Latin American Spanish
Latin Dictionary
Latin Grammar
Latvian
Letter Writing Skills
Life at 50: For Men
Life at 50: For Women
Life Coaching

Linguistics
LINUX
Lithuanian
Magic
Mahjong
Malay
Managing Stress
Managing Your Own Career
Mandarin Chinese
Mandarin Chinese Conversation
Marketing
Marx
Massage
Mathematics
Meditation
Middle East Since 1945, The
Modern China
Modern Hebrew
Modern Persian
Mosaics
Music Theory
Mussolini's Italy
Nazi Germany
Negotiating
Nepali
New Testament Greek
NLP
Norwegian
Norwegian Conversation
Old English
One-Day French
One-Day French – the DVD
One-Day German
One-Day Greek
One-Day Italian
One-Day Portuguese
One-Day Spanish
One-Day Spanish – the DVD
Origami
Owning a Cat
Owning a Horse
Panjabi
PC Networking for Small
  Businesses
Personal Safety and Self

Defence
Philosophy
Philosophy of Mind
Philosophy of Religion
Photography
Photoshop
PHP with MySQL
Physics
Piano
Pilates
Planning Your Wedding
Polish
Polish Conversation
Politics
Portuguese
Portuguese Conversation
Portuguese Grammar
Portuguese Phrasebook
Postmodernism
Pottery
PowerPoint 2003
PR
Project Management
Psychology
Quick Fix French Grammar
Quick Fix German Grammar
Quick Fix Italian Grammar
Quick Fix Spanish Grammar
Quick Fix: Access 2002
Quick Fix: Excel 2000
Quick Fix: Excel 2002
Quick Fix: HTML
Quick Fix: Windows XP
Quick Fix: Word
Quilting
Recruitment
Reflexology
Reiki
Relaxation
Retaining Staff
Romanian
Running Your Own Business
Russian
Russian Conversation
Russian Grammar

Sage Line 50
Sanskrit
Screenwriting
Second World War, The
Serbian
Setting Up a Small Business
Shorthand Pitman 2000
Sikhism
Singing
Slovene
Small Business Accounting
Small Business Health Check
Songwriting
Spanish
Spanish Conversation
Spanish Dictionary
Spanish Grammar
Spanish Phrasebook
Spanish Starter Kit
Spanish Verbs
Spanish Vocabulary
Speaking On Special Occasions
Speed Reading
Stalin's Russia
Stand Up Comedy
Statistics
Stop Smoking
Sudoku
Swahili
Swahili Dictionary
Swedish
Swedish Conversation
Tagalog
Tai Chi
Tantric Sex
Tap Dancing
Teaching English as a Foreign
  Language
Teams & Team Working
Thai
Theatre
Time Management
Tracing Your Family History
Training
Travel Writing

Trigonometry
Turkish
Turkish Conversation
Twentieth Century USA
Typing
Ukrainian
Understanding Tax for Small
  Businesses
Understanding Terrorism
Urdu
Vietnamese
Visual Basic
Volcanoes
Watercolour Painting
Weight Control through Diet &
  Exercise
Welsh
Welsh Dictionary
Welsh Grammar
Wills & Probate
Windows XP
Wine Tasting
Winning at Job Interviews
Word 2003
World Cultures: China
World Cultures: England
World Cultures: Germany
World Cultures: Italy
World Cultures: Japan
World Cultures: Portugal
World Cultures: Russia
World Cultures: Spain
World Cultures: Wales
World Faiths
Writing Crime Fiction
Writing for Children
Writing for Magazines
Writing a Novel
Writing Poetry
Xhosa
Yiddish
Yoga
Zen
Zulu

teach
yourself

managing stress
terry looker & olga gregson

- Do you want to understand the theory behind managing stress?
- Do you want to identify the sources of stress in your life?
- Are you looking for your own stress management plan?

Managing Stress is a step-by-step guide to dealing with stress, leading to a healthier, more relaxed and enjoyable way of life. The questionnaire to assess your stress levels will enable you to identify the signs, symptoms and sources of stress. You will understand what is happening to you mentally and physically and you will learn coping strategies to bring balance to your life.

Professor Terry Looker and **Dr Olga Gregson** are Fellows of the International Stress Management Association. They lecture at the Manchester Metropolitan University and worldwide and present stress management programmes for industry and the professions.

detox
denise whichello brown

- Would you like to feel re-energized, healthier and happier?
- Do you want to look good and gain optimum health?
- Would you like an easy-to-follow guide to help you detox?

Detox tells you all you need to know to feel great. Understand what detox is and take the questionnaire to discover just how much in need of a detox you are. Follow the simple 21-day plan, which includes recipes for all your meals. In order to feel revitalized and refreshed – and look better too! This book gives you invaluable information, and covers all aspects of detox – not only detoxing your body but your mind and spirit too. So why wait? Learn to detox now, and look forward to a new you!

Denise Whichello Brown has been practising for over 20 years and is internationally recognized as an accomplished practitioner and lecturer in the field of contemporary medicine.

fitness
jeff archer

- Do you want to learn how to get fit?
- Do you need to know how to make exercise part of daily life?
- Would you like to set and reach physical goals?

Can't find the time to get fit? Don't know where to start?
Fitness will show you how to formulate, set and stick to a
realistic exercise routine, whatever your age or ability. Covering
everything from staying motivated to eating sensibly and
avoiding injury, this book will help you stay fit with or without a
gym, and even with the family. Featuring exercises, information,
tips and tricks, this is all you need to get fit and stay that way.

Jeff Archer is a personal trainer and life coach, and a founder
and director of The Tonic, a lifestyle and fitness consultancy –
www.the-tonic.com.

teach
yourself

yoga
mary stewart

- Are you interested in the origins and history of yoga?
- Do you want to find out if yoga might be right for you?
- Would you like to make it part of your everyday life?

Yoga explains both the theory and practice of yoga. With clear, step-by-step illustrations it explains yoga breathing and meditation and shows you how to perform the poses, to promote flexibility and strength and relieve the stress of everyday living. Find out how this ancient system of meditation and exercise can transform your life!

Mary Stewart has been teaching yoga for over 30 years and is the author of five books on the subject.

teach
yourself

pilates
matthew aldrich

- Would you like to know more about Pilates and its benefits?
- Are you interested in improving your fitness and toning up?
- Do you want to find out why Pilates is so popular?

Pilates is an easy-to-follow introduction for everybody who wants to know more about the origins, theory and practice of this popular technique. Packed with useful exercises suitable for both newcomers and those already practising, this guide will ensure you benefit from all the health advantages that Pilates offers. This new edition is fully updated with a comprehensive introduction to abdominal exercises and the latest classes and resources.

Matthew Aldrich has been teaching and working within the health industry for over 17 years. The aim of this book and his work is to help you to get the most out of your body and your life.